A Complete Lowlife
Ed Brubaker

BLACK EYE BOOKS
Montreal, Canada

Black Eye Books, Publisher
5135 Parc Ave., Suite 5, Montreal, Quebec, Canada H2V 4G3

ISBN 0-9698874-7-7

Publication Design
by Michel Vrána with Ed Brubaker

Cover illustration by Ed Brubaker, watercolors by Brian Biggs

Printed and Bound in Canada

Author's note
by way of an introduction

The work in this books was done (sporadically) over a period of years, and I have a lot of affection for it, though in many places the art tends to hurt my eyes, but that's the nature of looking back on your work. One thing I wanted to say in this intro was how much I changed over the time I worked on these stories, and how when I started *Lowlife* my favorite writers were Bukowski and Kerouac, and now, while not to demean their achievements, they are far from my favorites. Another thing that occured to me was to address the whole autobiographical school of storytelling, and how, like the Catholics will tell you, a little confession can be good for the soul. But I don't know if I necessarily believe that, because sometimes, sitting down for hours and drawing scenes taken from some of the worst moments in your life can be pretty painful. And then there's the other people involved, your friends, (or ex-friends) who end up as cannon-fodder for your story, and let's face it, if it's your version of the truth (and you're changing all the names) what's the harm in changing the facts a little? Especially if it'll get a better reaction from the reader. So, shamefully, I will confess, that people (people who I loved and respected) have been hurt, by both the fiction and the non-fiction, and that was never my intention.

I also feel the need to point out that critics have always been wrong when they've accused me of playing up the main character (Tommy) for sympathy, that those scenes where he seems like an asshole or an idiot are the places where you're supposed to laugh at him. I've always found it funny that reviewers act as if autobiographical work doesn't go through any sort of creative process at all, and that the guy who shows himself being cheap all the time, and hitting his girlfriend, thinks he's showing himself at his finest and it's just an accident that it got put down on paper. From here I could go off in a number of directions, talking about the anecdotal nature of most true-life comics, or the sad state of the comics marketplace, but the only thing that really seems important is to acknowledge some people who've helped out in many different ways. First: Harvey Pekar and the Hernandez brothers –Gilbert, Jaime and Mario, who were all inspirations to me and who were all much kinder to me than I would have been; then: Carole Scott, Eric Shanower, Rob Williamson, Jason Lutes, Jon Lewis, Tom Hart, Dave Lasky, Mike Buckley and Mike Christian, Megan Kelso, James Sturm, Carlos Walker, Stefano Guadiano, Julie Doucet, Brian S., Steve Csutoras, Bob Schreck, Michel Vrana, and Lisa Maslowe. Finally, I'd like to thank my family for always being supportive of my interest in comics.

Ed Brubaker

San Francisco

CINÉMA VÉRITÉ

ED BRUBAKER · TOM HART

I WAS IN THE TENTH GRADE – MY FRIEND SCOTT AND I WERE AT A LATE MOVIE.

A FEW ROWS AHEAD OF US, A GUY WAS GETTING A **HANDJOB** FROM HIS GIRLFRIEND.

HUH HUH HUH HUH

WE WERE AMAZED...

OH MAN!

NO WAY!

HUH HUH H HUN HUH

HUH HUH HUH

AAAAAH

WHEN HE CAME, IT REALLY FLEW...

SPLUT

HA HA HA

HEY – WHO'S THROWING COKE?

HA HA HA HA HA HA HA HA

FOR YEARS AFTER THAT, "THROWING COKE" WAS AN INSIDE JOKE WITH US... IT WAS ALWAYS GOOD FOR A LAUGH...

HEY– YOU THROWING COKE IN THERE?

A TRUE STORY

ANOTHER ONE OF THOSE AMUSING ANECDOTES IN COMIC FORM THAT EVERY- ONE LIKES SO MUCH.

A Complete Lowlife

...THAT'S WHAT I'D DO... I'D JUS' TELL EVERYBODY I DIDN' DO IT! MY MOTHER... MY LAWYER...

UH... YEAH... THANKS...

A LIFE OF CRIME

Ed Brubaker '91

SOMETIMES I SEE MY LIFE AS A HAND REACHING OUT... JUST TAKING WHATEVER I CAN...

THE PAST

...FROM THE TIME I WAS A LITTLE KID I'VE BEEN LIKE THAT... STEALING CANDY AND COMICS AND STUFF...

UH... HEY KID!

IN SIXTH GRADE ME AND MY FRIEND EVAN USED TO SNEAK INTO PEOPLE'S GARAGES AND TAKE ALL THEIR EMPTY BOTTLES AND RETURN THEM FOR THE DEPOSITS...

SOMEHOW THIS LED TO VAN-DALISM...

WHAT ARE YOU DOING?

IT RUINS THE PAINT...

IN JUNIOR HIGH THIS GUY GREG AND I FOUND A VERY CONVENIENT LITTLE CAVE ON A HILL WHERE WE COULD THROW DIRT-CLODS AND ROCKS AT PASSING CARS IN RELATIVE SAFETY...

BUT THAT GOT OUT OF HAND ONE DAY WHEN GREG DARED ME TO THROW A BOTTLE AT A CAR...

C'MON... **WUSSY...**

...AND I HIT ONE... HARD.

CRASH!
SCREE

A MINUTE LATER WE WERE HIDING IN A TREE SCARED TO DEATH WHILE THE OWNER OF THE CAR SEARCHED FOR THE "LITTLE BASTARDS" WHO SMASHED HIS WINDOW...

DAMN
ERFUCK
CKSUCK
BITCH!!

HERE WE ARE...

THAT SAME YEAR MY BROTHER SCOTT AND ME AND EVAN AND HIS BROTHER WARREN ALL WENT TO THE FEDMART AND RIPPED—OFF CAP-GUNS, BUT SCOTT GOT GREEDY AND WENT BACK IN THE STORE FOR MORE CAPS AND THE NEXT THING I KNOW, WARREN'S RUNNING OUT SCREAMING...

SCOTT GOT **BUSTED!** RUN !!!

WE ALL RAN AND THREW OUR GUNS INTO A FIELD NEARBY...

REMARKABLY, SCOTT GOT TO KEEP HIS GUN AND MOST OF HIS CAPS BECAUSE HE SOMEHOW CONVINCED THE SECURITY GUARD THAT HE BOUGHT THEM AND WAS JUST STEALING THE EXTRA CAPS...

YEAH, HE SHOWED ME THAT STUFF ON HIS WAY IN...

SEE ?!

2

IN HIGH SCHOOL MY FRIENDS AND I DID SOME PRETTY OBNOXIOUS THINGS... LIKE STEALING TWELVE-PACKS OF BEER FROM SAFEWAY...

GO MAN!

... AND "DINE AND DASH"-ING...

OH... GOD DAMMIT!

...AND DOING LOTS OF DRUGS...

—SO I SAID "FUCK YOU IF YOU DON'T LIKE IT YOU CAN SUCK MY FUCKING DICK..." HAHAHA...OH MAN DID I TELL YOU HOW MY DAD BEAT ME UP THE OTHER DAY? I WAS IN MY ROOM... YOU'VE SEEN MY ROOM HAVEN'T YOU? SINCE I PAINTED IT—

RAMBLIN'

SNIFFF

BY TWELTH GRADE I WAS SELLING COKE ALMOST EVERYDAY IN GRAPHIC ART CLASS... WE'D GO INTO THE CAMERA-ROOM BECAUSE IT COULDN'T BE OPENED FROM THE OUTSIDE...

ALRIGHT MAN... IT LOOKS GOOD...

YOU GUYS DONE IN THERE?!

IT IS... AND IT'S PRACTICALLY UNCUT...

FULL OF SHIT.

CRAWFORD

CIRCLE JERKS

AROUND THIS TIME I GOT TURNED ONTO CRYSTAL ... A POWDERED SPEED. AT THE TIME IT WAS CHEAPER THAN COKE ...AND IT HAD A STRONGER RUSH AND LASTED LONGER, TOO. THE PROBLEM WITH IT WAS THAT THE COMEDOWN WAS AWFUL. SOMETIMES I COULDN'T EVEN EAT THE NEXT DAY...BUT THE RUSH WAS SO STRONG WHEN ADDED TO THE NEXT SIX HOURS OF FEELING LIKE YOU COULD SAY OR DO NO WRONG THAT I QUICKLY BECAME A FIEND FOR IT... I COULDN'T TURN IT DOWN...

BEEN UP WAY TOO LONG...

SKELETON CLUB 505/45 GRAVE

MY DEALING IN SCHOOL WAS STRICTLY SMALL-TIME THOUGH... JUST ENOUGH TO SUPPORT MY OWN DRUG USE AND AFTER HIGH SCHOOL MY CONNECTIONS DRIED UP AND I SPENT MANY CRAZED NIGHTS RUNNING ALL OVER TOWN TRYING TO SCORE SPEED ...WHICH LEADS UP TO THE STORY YOU'RE ABOUT TO READ...

NO?! ARE YOU KIDDING ME?!

3

THE IDEA | NOVEMBER, 1984...

IT'S NOT HAPPENING...

WHAT?!

WHY NOT?

HIS DEALER'S FLIPPIN' OUT...WON'T SELL ANYTHING LESS THAN A QUARTER OUNCE...

WELL **THAT** SUCKS!

IT WAS A PRETTY USUAL NIGHT...ME AND MY FRIEND SUNNY (WHO I WAS NOT-SO-SECRETLY IN LOVE WITH) AND OUR FRIEND PETER WERE OUT SEARCH-ING FOR CRYSTAL ...SOMETIMES IT WAS EASY, BUT MOST OF THE TIME WE ENDED UP DRIVING SOME GUY AROUND TO A BUNCH OF PLACES AND WAITING IN THE CAR FOR AN HOUR OR SO WHILE HE ATTEMPTED TO SCORE...

BUT THAT NIGHT WE HAD NO LUCK AT ALL, SO WE DROPPED SUNNY OFF AFTER FIVE HOURS OF DRIVING AROUND AND DECIDED TO GO HOME...

BYE.

BYE... I'LL CALL YOU TO-MORROW.

LATER SUNNY.

4

ON THE WAY TO PETER'S PLACE THE **IDEA** CAME...

SO WE'D NEED ABOUT THREE HUNDRED DOLLARS TO GET A QUARTER OUNCE, RIGHT?

YEAH?

...AND IF WE GOT A QUARTER WE COULD SELL $300 WORTH OR MORE AND **DO THE REST** AND THEN BUY ANOTHER QUARTER...OR WE COULD SELL EVEN **MORE** AND GET A **HALF OUNCE!**

YEAH, WELL... THAT SOUNDS **GREAT** BUT WE'VE ONLY GOT ABOUT FIFTY BUCKS TO OUR NAMES...

WHERE ARE WE GONNA GET THREE HUNDRED **BUCKS?**

THE PLAN

THE NEXT DAY I MET PETER AT HIS HOUSE TO TALK ABOUT HIS PLAN...

NOW, I'VE BEEN CHECKIN' THIS PLACE OUT FOR A COUPLE WEEKS...IT'D BE PRETTY **EASY,** I THINK...

WHAT ARE YOU TALKING **ABOUT?**

WE'RE GONNA ROB A COMPUTER STORE...

ARE YOU **KIDDING?!**

VANGE

NAW...IT'LL BE EASY... WE'LL GET A COUPLE DISK DRIVES, A KEYBOARD AND A BUNCH OF SOFT- WARE AND **THEN** WE'LL SELL IT AT A **USED** COMPUTER PLACE...

WHAT DO YOU MEAN BY "**ROB**" EXACTLY?

I MEAN WE'LL HOLD IT UP. YOU GO IN AND GET THE GUY INTO THE BACK ROOM AND HOLD A GUN ON HIM AND I'LL—

WAITAMINIT! I HOLD A GUN ON HIM?! I'M NOT HOLDING A **GUN** ON **ANYONE!**

5

YOU'RE TOTALLY OVER-REACTING! IT WON'T EVEN BE **LOADED**...YOU'VE **GOTTA** HOLD THE GUN BE-CAUSE HE WON'T RECOG-NISE YOU...HE'D RECOG-NISE **ME.** LOOK, WE'RE IN NO DANGER AT ALL...

ALL WE GOTTA DO IS STICK TO THE **PLAN**...NOW WILL YOU DO IT OR **NOT**?

I DON'T **KNOW**...WHAT'S THE **REST** OF THE PLAN?

HERE...LET ME SHOW YOU THIS DIAGRAM I MADE...

THE JOB

PETER'S PLAN WAS PRETTY WELL THOUGHT OUT AND I WASN'T EXACTLY THE HARDEST GUY TO CON-VINCE...I MEAN, WHEN YOU'VE BEEN TAKING WHATEVER YOU CAN GET YOUR HANDS ON MOST OF YOUR LIFE, THE MENTAL LEAP YOU HAVE TO MAKE FROM "STEALING" TO "ROBBING" IS LIKE JUMPING OVER A PUDDLE...SO A FEW NIGHTS LATER WE'RE IN THE ALLEY BEHIND THE COMPUTER STORE WAITING TO PULL THE JOB...

YOU GOT EVERYTHING? NO LAST MINUTE PROBLEMS?

NO. I GUESS NOT...

EVERYTHING WENT ACCORDING TO THE PLAN, PETER WAITED ACROSS THE STREET WHILE I WENT IN...

SOFTWARE VISTA

CIN

I ASKED THE GUY IF HE COULD SHOW ME A PRINTER...

HUH? OH YEAH... SURE.

SOFTWARE VISTA

6

...AND SINCE THE ONLY PRINTER WAS IN THE BACK-ROOM, HE TOOK ME TO THE BACK...WHERE I WOULD HOLD HIM AT GUN-POINT...

UNFORTUNATELY...

WHAT'S GOIN' ON?!

I DON'T KNOW... I COULDN'T **DO** IT. I THOUGHT I WAS GOING TO BUT I **FROZE**...

THIS **SUCKS**... YOU'VE **GOTTA** DO IT! I'D DO IT, BUT HE KNOWS ME... YOU'VE GOTTA GO **BACK**!

WHAT?!

I CHICKENED **OUT**. I CAN'T GO BACK! I CAN'T...

I THINK I DROPPED MY CAR KEYS...DID YOU FIND ANY..?

NO... I DIDN'T SEE ANY...

MAYBE IN THE BACK ROOM?

AMAZINGLY, WHEN I PULLED THE GUN OUT A CALM CAME OVER ME THAT I CAN'T EXPLAIN. I BECAME THE PERFECT ROBBER. THIS TIME EVERY- THING REALLY WENT ACCORDING TO THE PLAN...

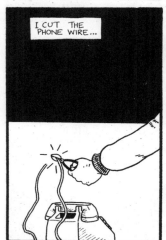

I CUT THE PHONE WIRE...

I MADE HIM PUT THE BACK ROOM KEYBOARD AND DISK DRIVE INTO A BAG...

THEN, WHILE PETER WAS IN THE FRONT ROOM GRABBING SOFTWARE AND A DISK DRIVE, I MADE HIM TAKE OFF HIS PANTS AND UNDERWEAR SO HE COULDN'T FOLLOW US...

7

... AND THEN WE LEFT.

WE DROVE AWAY JABBERING, AMAZED THAT WE HAD DONE IT AND RUSHING ON ADRENALINE...

—AND I COULD **NOT** BELIEVE HOW FUCKING CALM YOU SOUNDED... I WAS WATCHING THE THINKING, "WHAT'S WITH HIM?"

YEAH, I KNOW, I FELT LIKE I WAS JUST WATCHING THE WHOLE THING IT WAS—

I WAITED IN THE CAR WHILE PETER SOLD THE STUFF... WE HAD BARELY MADE IT TO THE STORE BEFORE CLOSING ...

HOW'D WE DO?

SIX HUN- DRED AND THIRTY DOLLARS ...

USED HARD AND SOFT

RIGHT **ON!**

THE LIE

THAT NIGHT WE WENT TO A SMALL PARTY AND EVEN THOUGH WE'D PROMISED EACH OTHER WE WOULDN'T TELL ANYONE, WE BOTH STARTED BRAGGING ALMOST IMMEDIATELY... WHEN SUNNY HEARD ABOUT IT SHE DRAGGED ME OUTSIDE...

YOU **IDIOT!**

WHAT?

WHAT WERE YOU THINKING? YOU KNOW YOU COULD GO TO **JAIL?!**

I'M NOT GONNA GO TO **JAIL!** THE GUY WILL NEVER SEE ME AGAIN AND I'VE GOT NO RECORD...HE **CAN'T** IDENTIFY ME...BUT I'M GONNA GET MY HAIR CUT JUST IN CASE...

YOU THINK IT'S THAT **SIMPLE**? WHAT ABOUT THOSE PEOPLE IN **THERE**?! SUPPOSE THEY **TELL**?

THEY WON'T. **GOD**, YOU WORRY TOO MUCH...IT'S NOT LIKE WE PULLED A **GUN** ON SOMEONE...I JUST KEPT THE GUY BUSY WHILE PETE RAN OFF WITH A BUNCH OF STUFF. I **CAN'T** GET IN TROUBLE...

WELL...**THAT'S** GOOD...I GUESS. I JUST DON'T WANT ANYTHING TO HAPPEN TO YOU...

JUST DON'T **WORRY**...

8

THE HEAD TRIP THE NEXT DAY I GOT MY HAIR CUT AND PETER AND I SCORED THE QUARTER OUNCE SURPRISINGLY EASILY... THE NEXT FOUR DAYS WERE A NON-STOP PARTY. WE'D DIVIDED THE DRUGS AND THE REST OF THE MONEY IN HALF...PETER WAS SELLING HIS STUFF BUT I WAS JUST DOING MINE WITH MY FRIENDS... ANY PLANS OF MAKING MONEY OFF THE WHOLE THING FORGOTTEN...

AFTER THE THIRD NIGHT WITHOUT SLEEP I FOUND MYSELF AT A PARTY WITH SUNNY AND OUR FRIEND JOHN. A GUY AT THE PARTY WAS SELLING ACID AND I TRADED HIM SOME SPEED FOR ACID AND TOOK TWO HITS ON THE SPOT...

HE'S TAKING THAT NOW?

TWENTY MINUTES LATER MY SPINE WAS TINGLING AND THINGS WERE STARTING TO PEEK AT ME OUT OF THE CORNERS OF MY EYES... THERE WAS THIS GIRL FRANCINE THERE WHO KEPT BADGERING ME TO GIVE HER SOME SPEED AND THE MORE SHE TALKED, THE MORE HER FEATURES BECAME UGLY AND WITCHLIKE.

ME ON ONE SO MUC OR YOU...YOU OWE ME... COME ON...

THE THING ABOUT ACID IS THAT IT CAN MAKE YOU SEE THINGS FROM THE OUTSIDE-IN, KIND OF... IT SOMETIMES MAKES YOU FEEL SUPERIOR TO EVERYONE ELSE WHEN YOU REALISE HOW STUPID MOST PEOPLE'S LIVES ARE, IT CAN MAKE IT HARD TO TAKE ANYONE ELSE SERIOUSLY UNLESS THEY'RE ON ACID, TOO... IT ALSO MAKES YOU LOOK AT YOUR-SELF THOUGH, AND SEE HOW MUCH YOU'RE WASTING YOUR LIFE AND WHAT YOU'VE DONE WRONG... AND THAT'S WHAT WAS HAPPENING TO ME...

JESUS... I HELD A GUN ON SOME-ONE... MY GOD... I HAVE NO SOUL...

SEE WHAT I MEAN?

FORTUNATELY, JOHN WAS A VETERAN DRUG-ADDICT AND KNEW A BAD TRIP WHEN HE SAW ONE, SO THEY GOT ME OUT OF THERE...

BUT FOR SOME REASON WHEN WE PULLED UP TO A STOP SIGN, I COULDN'T STAY IN THE CAR... I TOOK OFF RUNNING...

TOMMY!

I FLOPPED DOWN INTO SOME BUSHES AND STARED UP INTO THE SKY...

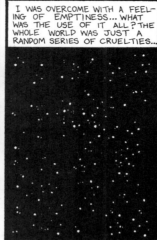

I WAS OVERCOME WITH A FEELING OF EMPTINESS... WHAT WAS THE USE OF IT ALL? THE WHOLE WORLD WAS JUST A RANDOM SERIES OF CRUELTIES...

...EVEN THE BUSHES AROUND ME SEEMED MENACING SOMEHOW...

AND THEN, JUST AS I WAS FEELING CERTAIN OF THE UTTER MEANINGLESSNESS OF MY EXISTENCE ... I WAS SHOWN... SOMETHING.

TOMMY!

WHAT?

IF THIS LOVELY GIRL COULD CARE FOR ME AT ALL...EVEN IF IT WASN'T EXACTLY THE WAY I WANTED... THAT HAD TO MEAN SOMETHING... DIDN'T IT?

HEY YOU... WHAT ARE YOU DOING? COME ON...

YOU SCARED ME, RUNNING OFF LIKE THAT... WHAT'S WRONG?

UH... I DON'T KNOW... NOTHING I GUESS...

10

WE DROPPED JOHN OFF AND SUNNY AND I HEADED OVER TO PETER'S PLACE TO COOL OUT A LITTLE... WHEN WE GOT THERE PETER WAS LOADING A COMPUTER INTO A CAR...

WHAT'S HE **DOING?**

I DON'T **KNOW**...

HEY MAN, ISN'T THAT YOUR **DAD'S** COMPUTER?

YEAH, IT **IS**... I SET UP THE PLACE TO MAKE IT LOOK LIKE SOMEONE BROKE IN... I'M GONNA SELL IT.

HE SAID IT SO FLAT... NO FEELING WHATSOEVER... AND HE MUST HAVE BEEN UP FOR DAYS, TOO, BECAUSE HE LOOKED LIKE HELL... AND HE KEPT STICKING HIS TONGUE IN AND OUT OF HIS MOUTH LIKE A FROG. I DON'T KNOW IF IT WAS THE ACID, BUT I REALLY FELT A DESIRE TO GET AWAY FROM HIM RIGHT THEN...

HE'S STEALING HIS DAD'S COMPUTER... HIS OWN **FUCKING FATHER**...

THAT'S **FUCKED!**

YEAH... BUT SOMEHOW IT'S NOT **TOO** SURPRISING...

11

THE FREAKOUT AFTER SLEEPING ON AND OFF FOR A FEW DAYS I WAS FEELING A LITTLE MORE SYMPATHETIC TO PETER, SO I WENT OVER TO SEE HOW HE WAS DOING...

PETE?

HEY PETER!

HEY!... HEY YOU!!

IT WAS BILL, PETER'S DAD... AND FROM THE LOOKS OF IT, HE WAS ON THE RAMPAGE...

RENE'S KEEP OUT!

HI BILL...

LOOKATCHERSELF!! YOU LOOK LIKE **SHIT**! YOU'VE BEEN UP ALL NIGHT ON **CRYSTAL**, HAVEN'TCHA?!

JESUS BILL, **NO**! I JUST WOKE **UP**!

BULLSHIT!!! YOU THINK I'M STUPID... BUT I'VE READ ALL ABOUT THIS **STUFF**...

...SO DON'T BOTHER **LYING** TO ME!!

I'M **NOT** LYING! I'VE BEEN SLEEPING!

FUCK **DAD**... GIVE HIM A BREAK...

12

13

A FUCKING THUG!!

SHUT UP.

BLAM!

C'MON MAN... JESUS!

HAH HA HA!

RENE'S KEEP OUT!

HEH...HA... HEH...

WHAT THE HELL IS **WRONG** WITH YOU?! ARE YOU **FUCKING NUTS**?!

THE LIE (REVISITED)

LATER THAT NIGHT

I WENT OVER TO SUNNY'S TO TELL HER ABOUT PETER AND HIS DAD...

...AND **THEN** HE'S SWINGING THE **GUN** AROUND... I HAD TO **DRAG** HIM OUT OF THERE...

THE GUN?

YEAH... THE ONE FROM THE ... FROM THE ... UH...

...ROBBERY...

14

FRANCINE WAS **RIGHT!** SHE SAID **YOU** HELD A **GUN!** YOU **LIED** TO ME! YOU **DID** USE A **GUN!**

NO... I ... UH... **SHIT**...

WHY DID YOU LIE TO **ME?**

I DON'T KNOW...

THE VISIT OVER THE NEXT FEW DAYS I TRIED TO CALL SUNNY, BUT GOT NO ANSWER... I WAS PRETTY BUMMED ABOUT THE WHOLE THING AND I WAS THINKING SOME CRYSTAL WOULD PICK UP MY SPIRITS, SO WHEN PETER CAME BY UNEXPECTEDLY IT DIDN'T REALLY BOTHER ME...

HEY MAN...

—AND THEN SHE SAID SHE WOULDN'T WANNA BE **ME** 'CUZ I HAVE TOO MANY **ZITS!**

MAN... THAT SUCKS...

YEAH... **HEY** I WAS THINKING WE SHOULD PULL ANOTHER **JOB**... I'M RUNNING PRETTY **LOW** AND I DON'T HAVE THE MONEY TO GET ANOTHER QUARTER...

ARE YOU SERIOUS?

YEAH, I SPENT MOST OF MY MONEY RENTING A ROOM. MY DAD ALMOST HAD ME **ARRESTED**... ANYWAY, I FIGURED WE COULD DO THE SAME STORE... IT WAS PRETTY EASY LAST TIME...

THE SAME PLACE?!

15

SURE, I CHECKED IT OUT THE OTHER DAY... HE HASN'T BEEFED UP HIS SECURITY AT **ALL**... WHY NOT?

JESUS MAN... I DON'T **THINK** SO... I DON'T KNOW...

THE TALK

THE NEXT DAY I WENT TO SEE MY FRIEND JAMES... HE HAD ALWAYS BEEN A PRETTY CLEAR THINKER SO I FIGURED HE COULD HELP ME OUT...

...SUNNY WON'T EVEN **TALK** TO ME AND NOW **THIS**, TOO...

...I JUST DON'T KNOW WHAT TO **DO**...

WHAT'S THE PROBLEM? JUST TELL HIM "NO WAY..."

IT'S NOT THAT SIMPLE, IT'S LIKE THERE'S SOME SORT OF **BOND** BE-TWEEN ME AND HIM NOW, 'CUZ WE DID IT TOGETHER... LIKE IN THAT MOVIE "DOUBLE INDEMNITY", WHEN TWO PEOPLE PULL A CRIME TOGETHER, THEY'RE STUCK WITH EACH OTHER... THEY HAVE TO RIDE IT OUT TOGETHER...

IN OTHER WORDS, IF HE GETS CAUGHT YOU'LL GET BUSTED TOO?

BASICALLY...

WELL, I DUNNO... SOUNDS LIKE YOU FUCKED-UP BIG-TIME. YOU GOT ALL INTO CRYSTAL AND WENT **WAY** OVERBOARD... ARMED ROBBERY... **FUCK**...

WHAT, HAVEN'T YOU EVER STOLEN ANY-THING?

SURE... REMEMBER THAT ART STORE I WAS WORKING AT FOR A WHILE LAST YEAR?

YEAH..?

"WELL, I WAS GETTING REAL BORED WITH THAT JOB AND FEELING LIKE I WAS BEING TREATED LIKE SHIT THERE... SO I STARTED TAKING STUFF... PENS... BRUSHES... PAPER... JUST LITTLE THINGS AT FIRST... BUT I WAS STILL PRETTY SCARED OF GETTING CAUGHT...

GOOD ART STORE

CLOSED

STRATHMORE

"I GOT OVER THAT PRETTY QUICK THOUGH, BECAUSE THEN I TOOK A WHOLE **FUCKING** TABLE AND A LIGHT FOR IT AND A CHAIR AND EVERYTHING... AND IT WAS **EASY!**

The Stolen Goods...

"AFTER THAT IT GOT REALLY BAD... I STARTED TO MAKE IT LIKE A GAME... SEEING HOW MUCH I COULD GET AWAY WITH, RIGHT IN FRONT OF THE OTHER WORKERS...

SEEYA' TOMORROW.

LATER...

$12.00 LIGHTBOX

"ONE TIME I EVEN GOT THE MANAGER TO HELP ME CARRY OUT SOME BAGS THAT HAD OVER A HUNDRED DOLLARS WORTH OF PAINTS IN 'EM TO MY CAR... THAT WAS WHEN I KNEW I'D GONE TOO FAR, SO I QUIT THE JOB 'CUZ I KNEW I'D NEVER STOP STEALIN' 'CUZ IT WAS TOO EASY..."

HERE YOU GO...

THANKS...

STORE

ARM

BUT **SEE**? THAT'S THE DIFFERENCE THERE... I KNEW WHEN TO STOP... YOU OBVIOUSLY **DON'T**...

WHAT CAN I **SAY**? IT SEEMED LIKE A GOOD IDEA AT THE TIME...

⑰

IF I WERE YOU I'D TRY TO TALK PETER OUT OF DOING ANYTHING ELSE AND THEN JUST STAY **AWAY** FROM HIM... I MEAN HE'S OBVIOUSLY **NUTS**...

HE'S NOT **THAT** BAD... HE'S JUST OUT OF CONTROL RIGHT NOW... I DON'T KNOW... WHAT SHOULD I DO ABOUT **SUNNY**?

ARE YOU SLEEPING WITH HER YET?

NO... JUST FRIENDS...

WELL... SHIT... I DUNNO...

THE PHONE CALL

A COUPLE DAYS LATER I FINALLY GOT SUNNY ON THE PHONE, BUT SHE DIDN'T REALLY WANT TO TALK TO ME TOO MUCH...

AW C'MON... YOU'RE NOT STILL MAD AT ME... ARE **YOU**?

I JUST DON'T LIKE BEING LIED TO... THAT'S ALL.

WELL I'M SORRY... I JUST DIDN'T KNOW HOW YOU'D FEEL... AND I DIDN'T WANT TO RUIN MY CHANCES WITH YOU...

WHAT ARE YOU TALKING ABOUT!? YOUR "CHANCES?" WE'RE JUST **FRIENDS!**

IS THAT ALL WE'RE **EVER** GOING TO BE?

I DON'T KNOW...

18

...PROBABLY...

AFTER THAT DAY I DIDN'T SEE OR TALK TO SUNNY FOR A LONG TIME...

THE FUCK-UP THAT NIGHT I MET PETER AT A TACO STAND WE USED TO HANG OUT AT A LOT... I WAS GOING TO TRY TO TALK SOME SENSE INTO HIM...

ACAPULCO TACO SHOP

WHAT THE HELL ARE YOU TALKING ABOUT?!

I'M NOT GONNA DO IT... AND YOU SHOULDN'T EITHER. YOU'RE GONNA FUCK IT UP AND THEN YOU'LL GO TO FUCKING **JAIL!**

THAT'S BULLSHIT! I WON'T FUCK IT **UP!!** YOU'RE JUST A **PUSSY!!**

I'M **NOT** A PUSSY! I'M JUST NOT STUPID!

CHECK OUT THE FAGS... HAVIN' A CATFIGHT...

WHAT?! HEY **FUCK YOU DICKWEED!**

JESUS PETER, JUST IGNORE THEM... DON'T BE AN IDIOT...

BETTER LISTEN TO YOUR GIRL-FRIEND OR YOU'LL GET YOUR ASS KICKED...

SUCK MY DICK!!

19

C'MON MAN... LET'S GET THE HELL OUTTA HERE...

NO WAY! WE CAN TAKE THESE GUYS... THEY'RE JUST A BUNCH OF FUCKIN' REDNECKS!

WHAT THE HELL IS YOUR PROBLEM?! LET'S GET THE FUCK OU—

-TOOF!

I LOOKED UP FROM THE GROUND KIND OF DAZED AND I SAW PETER HOLDING HIS GUN...

I GUESS MY SURVIVAL INSTINCT TOOK OVER THEN BECAUSE AS SOON AS THAT GUY HIT THE GROUND I WAS RUNNING AS FAST AS I COULD TO THE CAR...

20

I LOOKED BACK AND SAW THE OTHER TWO GUYS ATTACKING PETER... HE WASN'T EVEN FIGHTING BACK...

AND A FEW FEET AWAY THEIR FRIEND WAS JUST LYING THERE DEAD...

SHIT... WHAT SHOULD I **DO?** I CAN'T JUST LEAVE HIM THERE...

WEEEOOOW

OHFUCK THE **COPS!!** I GUESS I **CAN** LEAVE HIM THERE... I'M OUTTA HERE... SHIT...

THE REST A FEW DAYS LATER I WAS PICKED UP ON AN ARMED ROBBERY CHARGE...

IT TURNED OUT THAT SUNNY HAD BEEN RIGHT, ONE OF THE PEOPLE AT THAT PARTY HAD TOLD THE COPS ABOUT US TO GET A REDUCED SENTENCE ON A DRUG DEALING CHARGE.

BUT SOMETIMES I THINK I MUST BE THE LUCKIEST GUY IN THE WORLD BECAUSE THE GUY AT THE STORE COULDN'T IDENTIFY EITHER OF US IN A PHOTO-LINE-UP SO THEY HAD TO DROP THE CHARGES AGAINST US...

WHEW!

OF COURSE, THEY STILL HAD PETER ON A POSSIBLE MURDER RAP... UNBELIEVABLY, THEY OFFERED TO LET HIM GO SCOT FREE IF HE WOULD TURN ME IN, SINCE HE WAS A MINOR AND I WASN'T, BUT HE WOULDN'T DO IT... I GUESS IN A LOT OF WAYS I OWE HIM MY LIFE...

PETER ENDED UP SERVING THREE YEARS ON A COUNTY WORK FARM FOR SECOND DEGREE MANSLAUGHTER... FOR THE LAST TWO YEARS HE TAUGHT THE OTHER CONS HOW TO USE COMPUTERS AND THE STATE PAID HIM THIRTEEN DOLLARS AN HOUR. HE SAVED THE MONEY AND WHEN HE GOT OUT HE MOVED TO ARIZONA AND OPENED A PIZZA JOINT. LAST I HEARD HE WAS DOING PRETTY WELL... SAYS HE'D NEVER GET INTO DRUGS OR CRIME EVER AGAIN...

21

THE EPILOGUE

FEB. 1991... AS FOR ME, I'D HAVE TO SAY MY DRUG USING DAYS ARE MOSTLY OVER, TOO... I'M NOT TRYING TO SOUND PREACHY OR ANYTHING, IF YOU WANT TO DO DRUGS THAT'S YOUR BUSINESS... MY LIFE JUST WORKS BETTER WITHOUT THEM...

THAT'S ME THERE, CLOSING UP THE DRY-CLEANERS I WORK AT...

REMEMBER WHAT I SAID BEFORE ABOUT BEING THE LUCKIEST GUY IN THE WORLD? WELL, HERE'S MORE PROOF OF THAT... AFTER ABOUT THREE YEARS OF NOT SEEING SUNNY, I RAN INTO HER ON THE STREET AND WE STARTED TALKING AND THE NEXT THING YOU KNOW WE'RE DATING EACH OTHER. WE WENT BACK AND FORTH FOR ABOUT SIX MONTHS AND THEN WE JUST DECIDED TO MOVE IN TOGETHER AND IT'S BEEN LIKE THAT FOR ABOUT A YEAR AND A HALF NOW...

I MEAN SURE, IT'S NOT ALWAYS PERFECT, BUT JUST THINK ABOUT IT... I GOT AWAY WITH ALL THIS STUFF, AND I STILL GOT THE GIRL...THE FIRST GIRL I WAS EVER REALLY IN LOVE WITH... IF THAT'S NOT LUCKY I DON'T KNOW WHAT IS... HERE SHE COMES NOW...

HEY...WHY DON'T I TAKE US OUT TO DINNER TONIGHT?

WHERE DID YOU GET MONEY? I THOUGHT YOU WERE BROKE...

I WAS...

YOU...

WHAT CAN I SAY? I GUESS SOME HABITS ARE JUST HARDER TO BREAK THAN OTHERS...

THE END

the Girlfriend an

JULY, 1987...

SHE WONDERS IF SHE'S LIKE HER MOM. SHE WORRIES ABOUT THAT A LOT...

HER MOM USED TO ABANDON HER AND HER BROTHER AND GO OFF WITH STRANGE MEN. SHE'D LEAVE THEM ALONE FOR DAYS... SOMETIMES WEEKS. SHE HAD TO PRACTICALLY RAISE HER LITTLE BROTHER HERSELF.

WHEN SHE WAS IN JUNIOR HIGH HER DAD SENT HER PICTURES A PRIVATE DETECTIVE HAD TAKEN OF HER MOM HAVING SEX WITH TWO MEN AT THE SAME TIME. ONE OF THEM WAS THE MAN WHO HAD SOLD THEM THEIR TRAILER.

SHE WONDERS IF WE'RE ALL DOOMED TO FAIL THE SAME WAY OUR PARENTS DO. SHE THINKS SHE TRIES HARD NOT TO MAKE HER MOTHER'S MISTAKES, BUT SHE ALWAYS DOES ANYWAY. SHE THINKS:

SHIT.

1

Ed Brubaker '94

ANNIE?

OF COURSE SHE'S NOT HOME. HE KNEW SHE WOULDN'T BE...HE KNOWS EXACTLY WHERE SHE IS. BUT STILL, THERE WAS A SLIGHT HOPE.

HE TRIES NOT TO THINK ABOUT WHAT SHE'S ACTUALLY DOING, BUT HE CAN'T STOP IMAGES FROM APPEARING IN HIS HEAD...HE HOPES HIS IMAGINATION IS WORSE THAN THE TRUTH.

THE THING THAT REALLY GETS HIM IS THAT HE INTRODUCED THEM. IT'S NOT LIKE THIS IS THE FIRST TIME SHE'S CHEATED ON HIM, BUT SOMEHOW IT'S **WORSE**...

GLIP GLIP GLIP

OLD ENG 8

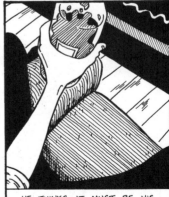

HE THINKS IT MUST BE HIS WEAKNESS THAT MAKES HER NEED OTHER MEN. HE THINKS HE ISN'T "MAN" ENOUGH TO KEEP HIS WOMAN.

②

24

WHAT DID I DO THAT WAS SO WRONG? IT'S NOT LIKE I'M MARRIED TO TOMMY OR ANYTHING...

HE DOESN'T OWN ME.

YET STILL, SHE'S WORRIED ABOUT HURTING HIM. EARLIER TONIGHT SHE WAS SURE SHE SAW JAMES, TOMMY'S BEST FRIEND. IF HE TOLD TOMMY, IT'D KILL HIM, SHE THINKS.

SHE'S CHEATED ON HIM FOUR TIMES NOW, AND HE ALWAYS ACTS SO UNDERSTANDING AND FORGIVING. THE FIRST TIME WAS WITH HIS HIGH SCHOOL BEST FRIEND AND IT DESTROYED THEIR FRIENDSHIP... YET HE FORGAVE HER. SHE WONDERS:

WHAT THE HELL IS WRONG WITH HIM? WHY DOES HE PUT UP WITH IT?

SHE REMEMBERS BEING TWELVE AND HER MOM TELLING HER THAT MEN ONLY LIKED GIRLS WHO HAD SEX WITH THEM. SHE THINKS, "WHY WOULD ANYONE SAY THAT TO THEIR KID?"

3

CHRIST, IS SHE EVEN GONNA COME HOME?

...HE THINKS. HE WONDERS WHAT HE'LL DO WHEN SHE DOES. HOW IS HE SUPPOSED TO REACT?

SHE HAD SAID SHE WAS GOING TO A PARTY WITH HER FRIEND MARY, BUT HE DIDN'T BELIEVE HER, SO HE WENT OVER TO MARY'S HIMSELF. SHE TRIED TO COVER FOR ANNIE, BUT IT WAS OBVIOUS SHE WAS LYING...

OH, REALLY? SHE WENT TO HER MOM'S, HUH? THERE'S NO ONE HOME THERE...

WELL... I THINK THEY WERE GOING OUT TO DINNER... OR SOMETHING...

LOOKING AT HER GARDEN, HE'S AMAZED THAT SOMEONE SO NURTURING CAN BE SO DESTRUCTIVE, TOO. SHE HAD WORKED FOR DAYS TO CLEAR AWAY THE WEEDS AND PLANT A REAL GARDEN. "THAT'S REALLY IMPRESSIVE," BILLY HAD SAID. BILLY WASN'T EASILY IMPRESSED.

WHEN HE WAS IN HIGH SCHOOL HE WAS CONVINCED HE'D NEVER HAVE ANYONE REALLY LOVE HIM. HE DIDN'T KNOW HOW TO TALK TO GIRLS THE WAY OTHER GUYS DID. HE'D FELT DESPERATE THEN.

WHEN HE AND ANNIE FELL IN LOVE HE WAS COMPLETELY SURPRISED. HE FELT HAPPY AND SECURE FOR THE FIRST TIME... AT LEAST FOR A WHILE HE DID.

YEARS FROM NOW HE'LL REALIZE THAT THIS RELATIONSHIP WAS BASED MORE ON FEAR THAN LOVE. HIS FEAR THAT HE IS UNLOVEABLE...

4

TONIGHT SHE MADE LOVE WITH ETHAN UNDER A TREE AND IT WAS BEAUTIFUL. MORE BEAUTIFUL THAN ANYTHING SHE AND TOMMY HAVE DONE IN MONTHS.

BUT TOMORROW ETHAN WILL BE BACK IN NEW YORK AND SHE'LL STILL BE HERE, IN HER LIFE.

SHE WONDERS IF TOMMY WOULD BREAK-UP WITH HER IF HE KNEW...

HEY, MEOW-MEOW...

SHE DOESN'T THINK HE WOULD, AND SOMEHOW THAT REALLY BOTHERS HER.

SHIT...

MARY'LL TELL HER I CAME BY TONIGHT... I MIGHT AS WELL JUST CONFRONT HER... FUCK!

HE KNEW HER HISTORY WELL ENOUGH TO KNOW THIS WOULD HAPPEN. BUT LIKE WOODY ALLEN SAID, "YOU ALWAYS THINK YOU'LL BE THE ONE TO CHANGE THEM." BUT YOU NEVER ARE.

HE CAN'T JUST LET THIS GO, HE HAS TO DO SOMETHING. HE'S JUST SO SCARED THAT HE'LL NEVER FIND ANYONE ELSE WHO'LL LOVE HIM... AND HE FEELS STUPID FOR BEING THAT WAY.

CLICK...
CLAK...

CLIK

HI...

6

DID YOU FUCK HIM?

UH... WHAT?

WHO?

ETHAN.

FUCK.

UM... DID JAMES CALL YOU..?

NO. DOES HE KNOW?! THAT'S JUST FUCKING GREAT, ANNIE!!

WHY?! WHAT'S YOUR FUCKIN' PROBLEM?!!

ARE YOU GONNA DO SOMETHING?

7

WHAT ?!

I SAID, "ARE YOU GONNA DO SOMETHING?" ARE YOU, OR ARE YOU JUST GONNA POUT?

WHAT AM I SUPPOSED TO DO ABOUT IT?

I DON'T KNOW... ...SOMETHING.

FUCK YOU.

DO YOU STILL LOVE ME?

I GUESS SO...

YOU STILL WANT ME? YES.

AFTER EVERYTHING? YES...

8

IT'S BEEN TWO WEEKS SINCE SHE LEFT. HE WONDERS IF SHE'LL COME BACK AGAIN THIS TIME. HE WONDERS IF HE'D EVEN WANT HER TO.

"THERE MUST HAVE BEEN SOME-THING I COULD HAVE DONE OR SAID," HE THINKS FOR THE HUN-DRED AND SIXTEENTH TIME, NOT KNOWING WHAT HE MEANS BY IT EXACTLY.

SOMEWHERE INSIDE HE KNOWS THAT THE THINGS THEY BOTH DID AND SAID WERE DECIDED FOR THEM A LONG TIME AGO... BUT THERE IS A HOPE – AN OPTIMISM THAT HE FEELS, THAT HE CAN ESCAPE THIS...

HE LOOKS AROUND HIS HOME FOR A FEW MINUTES AND HE THINKS:

JESUS, SOMEONE SHOULD CLEAN THIS PLACE UP A BIT...

END

HELLO?...OH HI! WHAT'S UP? I WAS JUST THINKING ABOUT — **WHAT?** OH... SURE... FINE... HOLD ON...

MARNIE'S ON THE PHONE FOR **YOU**, BILLY!

OH... THANKS.

MUST BE BLIND LOVE ♪ ONLY KIND ♪ LOVE IS STONE

BLIND LOVE KIND 'A LOVE

AH...**FUCK OFF!!**

WHAT'S WRONG WITH YOU MAN? WHAT ARE YOU WAITING OUT HERE FOR?

AH...MARNIE CALLED FOR BILLY...THEY'VE BEEN TALKING A LOT SINCE WE STOPPED GOING OUT... I GUESS IT JUST BUGS ME... YOU KNOW.

WELL, YOU ALWAYS DO THIS... YOU'VE GOT NO RIGHT TO BE MAD. YOU WEREN'T REALLY GOING OUT WITH HER ANYWAY, YOU KNOW? YOU WERE JUST HAVING SEX WITH HER FOR A FEW WEEKS...

2

...BESIDES YOU ONLY LIKED HER BECAUSE SHE LOOKED JUST LIKE ANNIE AND THAT'S STUPID TO BEGIN WITH!

YEAH? WELL FUCK YOU ANYWAY...

ABOUT NINETEEN MILES NORTH OF MAYNARDVILLE LIES THE TOWN OF 'DAWN SPRINGS.' DAWN SPRINGS WAS ONCE A NICE PLACE... THEN IT BECAME A COLLEGE TOWN. THE GOOD PART OF THIS, THOUGH IS THAT 'COLLEGE TOWNS HAVE 'NIGHTCLUBS,' AND SINCE MAYNARDVILLE IS SADLY (OR MAYBE NOT SO SADLY) LACKING SUCH AN ESTABLISHMENT, THE YOUNG PEOPLE USUALLY HEAD NORTH ON WEEKEND NIGHTS.

DAWN SPRINGS

HWY 991

MAYNARD VILLE

HEY MAN, CHILL OUT ON THE WHISKEY! I THOUGHT YOU SAID YOU DIDN'T WANT TO GET DRUNK...

I'M JUST GONNA GET A LITTLE BUZZED... THAT'S ALL...

WELL HERE, GIMME THAT AND LET'S GO. IT'S ALMOST 10:30!

HEY! I'M NOT EVEN BUZZED AT ALL!

YOU GOT THE BOTTLE UNDER YOUR SWEATER ...RIGHT?

YEAH... CALM DOWN... FUCK.

I AM CALM. FUCK YOU.

JESUS CHRIST SALLY! IT'S MY I.D.! HOW MANY TIMES DO I HAVE TO APOLOGIZE TO YOU?!

YOU MUST HAVE A

WHAT TOOK YOU SO LONG?

AH, SALLY WAS GIVING ME A HARD TIME 'CUZ OF THAT TIME I TRIED TO PICK-UP ON HER...

OH...WELL DON'T DRINK ALL OF THIS... I'M GONNA GO DANCE.

3

35

36

♪1... 2... 3 GIRL♪ WE SURE DO ♪GOT A ♪LOT... ♪OH D♪

I REFUSE TO DANCE TO THIS SEVENTIES REHASH BULLSHIT...

WHAT'S GOING ON HERE?

...WELL I WANT TO KNOW WHAT HAPPENED! THIS IS MY **ART** GODDAMN IT!

A+P BOWL

JUST CALM DOWN. IT'S NOT THAT BIG A DEAL.

IT IS TO ME! I WENT TO PEE AND I COME BACK AND THIS IS WHAT I GET TO SEE...

AH HA HA HA!

SEE! PEOPLE ARE LAUGHING AT ME!

THEY'RE NOT LAUGHING AT YOU... THEY'RE LAUGHING AT THE PAINTING...

...HEH...HEH...

HEH...HEH... YOU MISSED IT MAN! SOMEONE PAINTED 'DICKS' ON ALL THE DANCERS IN THAT STUPID PAINTING... ...HEH...

OH REALLY?

NOW I WONDER WHO THE HELL COULD HAVE DONE THAT?!

YOU FUCKER! YOU **DID** IT, DIDN'T YOU?

5

...MAYBE I DID, MAYBE I DIDN'T...

JESUS MAN! KEEP THAT DOWN... YOU WANT TO GET THROWN OUT?

THIS IS ALMOST EMPTY! NO WONDER YOU'RE VANDALIZING THINGS...

HEY JAMES, CHECK THIS OUT! THEY'VE GOT A FUCKING BAND!

YEAH...IT WAS ON THE FLYER. I THINK THEY CALL THEM- SELVES "THE BEATNIK WARRIORS."

MOD PUNK MOD PUNK & SUCKS!

BEATNIK WARRIORS

THAT'S THEM. IT'S JUST TWO GUYS WITH "GO-TEE'S"... THEY DON'T EVEN HAVE A GUITAR PLAYER! AND THIS CROWD IS EATING IT UP... I DON'T BELIEVE THIS...

-CHICKA-BOOM-CHICK

Wimpy drum machine noise ♪

HEY... YOU GUYS FUCKIN' SUCK!!

PUNK MOD PUNK MOD PUNK SUCKS!

OKAY LOUDMOUTH. THAT'S IT. SIT DOWN AND SHUT UP! I DON'T WANT ANY MORE TROUBLE.

WELL THEY FUCKIN' SUCK AND THAT'S ALL THERE IS TO IT... YOU KINDA SUCK TOO...

MANUAL SCAN

WHITE TRASH

YEAH YEAH...

6

38

AT THIS POINT THE REST OF THE NIGHT WAS HIGHLIGHTED BY THREE MIND-NUMBINGLY BRIGHT MOVES, WHICH WILL BE LABELLED APPROPRIATELY... IT ALL BEGINS AS THE BAND IS CLEARING THE STAGE AND TOMMY IS MAKING PITIFULLY DRUNKEN ATTEMPTS AT PICKING-UP ON GIRLS...

CAN EVERYONE PLEASE RESIST THE TEMPTATION TO DANCE ON THE STAGE WHILE THE BAND IS CLEARING IT?!

WARRIORS

NO...WAIT SERIOUSLY... I JUST WANT TO SHOW YOU THE ROOF OF MY CAR...

♪"I GOT ANTS IN MY PANTS AN'

AW...COME ON...I —

I NEED TO DANCE...♪♫♪

HEY?

♪SO WHAT 'CHA GONNA DO...♪

THAT'S JAMES BROWN! WHERE'S A GOOD PLACE TO GET FUNKY?

I GOT♪ ♪ANTS IN MY♫ PANTS AN'

HEY HOODOO! GET RID OF THIS GUY!

WARRI

SIR? COULD YOU PLEASE REMOVE YOURSELF FROM THE STAGE?!

HUH?

BRIGHT MOVE #1: GIVING THE FINGER TO THE DJ/MANAGER OF THE CLUB.

7

40

FUCK THAT SHIT...

WAS THAT A COP?

WHAT THE HELL ARE YOU STILL UP FOR, YOU BIG OLD METRIC CONVERSION HEAD ?!

SHUT UP...

SO WHAT HAPPENED TO YOU ?

AH... I GOT THROWN OUT AND BEAT UP...

SO I GUESS YOU DIDN'T SCORE ?

NOPE. I GUESS NOT...

HEY! YOU'VE BEEN TALKIN' TO MARNIE FOR ABOUT FOUR HOURS HAVEN'T YOU ?!

10

SLAM

WHAT THE HELL DID I DO LAST NIGHT? I FEEL LIKE HELL... HOPE I DIDN'T DO ANYTHING TOO STUPID...

DID I DRIVE MYSELF HOME? GOD I HOPE NOT...

I THINK I MIGHT HAVE COME HOME WITHOUT JAMES. WONDER IF HE GOT A RIDE WITH A GIRL OR SOMETHING ...

...NO, FIRST I'LL TIE HIM UP...NO, I'LL HIT HIM WITH A BAT A FEW TIMES THEN TIE HIM UP... AND I'LL BRING OVER HIS EX-GIRLFRIEND AND...

MAYNARDVILLE NEXT EXIT ONE MILE

THE END

IT'S NO BIG DEAL... I HAD TO WAIT OUT THERE ALL THE **TIME** BEFORE I GOT MY KEY...

UH... YEAH...

YOU **JERK** ...AT LEAST YOU WERE GETTING PAID!

SLAM!!

INTO THE OFFICE ALREADY... THAT WAS FAST...

OFFICE

DO NOT DISTURB

AND THANK **GOD**... I DON'T NEED HIM OUT HERE IN MY WAY...

THIS PLACE IS TRASHED... JESUS...

OFFICE

DO NOT DISTURB

SCI-

TION

OF **COURSE**...IT'S ALWAYS THE SCI-FI SECTION THAT'S THE WORST...FUCKIN' SCIENCE FICTION GEEKS...STILL, IT'S THE SCI-FI AND FANTASY BOOKS THAT KEEP THE STORE IN BUSINESS I GUESS...NOT LIKE ANYTHING ELSE REALLY SELLS...

SIRENS TITAN

TWENTY MINUTES LATER...

THERE... THAT'S A LOT BETTER...

DO NOT DISTURB

HEY TOMMY?

OFFIC

DO NOT

DISTUR

3

47

I GOT A C.O.D. FOR $148.50...

OH... C.O.D. HUH? **GREAT**... LEMME SEE IF I CAN GET A CHECK...

DICK, I NEED A CHECK FOR $148.50 FOR A C.O.D. FROM INGRAM.

WHAT ?! C.O.D. !? I MISS TWO LOUSY PAYMENTS AND THEY START SHIPPING C.O.D. ?

THOSE BASTARDS...

SO...DO YOU WANT THE BOOKS OR NOT ?

YES! HERE! GIVE THEM THEIR MOTHER-FUCKING **CHECK** AND TELL THEM TO SHOVE IT UP THEIR FUCKING GODDAMN **ASSHOLES !!!**

JESUS...

SCI-FI

CLICK

OH **BOY**... ANOTHER STEPHEN KING BOOK... JUST WHAT THE WORLD NEEDS...

IT'S **MISSING!**

WHAT?

THE $300 ROBERT E. HOWARD BOOK THAT WAS ON MY FUCKING **DESK!** IT'S GONE AND THERE'S NO BIG SALE LIKE THAT ON THE WEEK-END RE-CEIPTS!

IT'S BEEN **STOLEN!!**

4

48

WE DON'T **KNOW** THAT IT'S BEEN STOLEN... LOOK, LET ME LOOK AROUND AND CALL DAVE AND SEE WHAT HAPPENED TO IT...

YEAH... FINE...

...BUT I'M SURE IT'S BEEN STOLEN... JUST LIKE EVERYTHING ELSE I'VE EVER HAD OF VALUE... SIGH...

GOD...WHAT A HOPELESS PARANOID...

NOT THAT HE DOESN'T HAVE GOOD REASON TO DISTRUST PEOPLE THOUGH...

AFTER ALL THE SHIT THAT'S HAPPENED TO HIM... FIRST HE LET TIM RIVERA BECOME A PARTNER IN THE STORE WITHOUT PUTTING IN ANY MONEY...AND THE GUY ROBBED HIM BLIND AND LEFT HIM ASS-DEEP IN DEBT TO HIS DISTRIBUTORS...

...AND THEN JUST AFTER HE GETS HIMSELF OUT OF THAT HE FINDS OUT RUFUS, HIS OLD MANAGER, IS STEALING BOOKS **AND** MAKING AMAZING DEALS TO PEOPLE SO HE CAN GET A BONUS EVERYDAY...

HEY, YOU'RE A "BEAT GENERATION" FAN AREN'TCHA? HERE'S A ONE-TIME-ONLY OFFER. A 1ST PRINTING OF "ON THE ROAD" FOR ONLY $50.⁰⁰ **IF** YOU BUY IT TODAY...

RIGHT ON! THANKS A LOT, MAN!

...AND THEN ON TOP OF THAT A MONTH LATER CURTIS, AN OLD FRIEND OF HIS, IS CAUGHT BREAKING INTO THE STORE AND STEALING OVER $2000 WORTH OF RARE BOOKS...

AW MAN...

...ADD ALL THAT TO THE AMOUNT OF POT HE'S SMOKED OVER THE LAST TWENTY YEARS AND IN SOME WAYS I GUESS IT'S AMAZING HE'S DOING AS WELL AS HE IS...

5

I FOUND THE **BOOK**. IT'S IN THE LAY-AWAY BOX, SOME GUY NAMED MARVIN PUT FIFTY BUCKS DOWN ON IT AND HE'S GONNA PAY THE REST OFF NEXT WEEK.

OH... THAT'S GREAT... THANKS A LOT, I REALLY THOUGHT IT WAS GONE...

YEAH... I **KNOW**.

WELL, I'M GONNA GET OUTTA HERE ... I MAY OR MAY NOT BE IN TO-MORROW...

OKAY...

THANK GOD... NOW I CAN RELAX.

WE'RE [EN]

LATER THAT NIGHT...

FORTY... SIXTY... EIGHTY... NOT A BAD DAY... $480.00 ... NOT GREAT, BUT OH **WELL**...

... AND AN EXTRA TWENTY FOR ME IN VOIDED-OUT SALES... NO, NOT A BAD DAY AT ALL...

SORRY WE'RE CLOSED

KA-KLIK

GOD...IT SURE WOULDN'T HELP DICK'S PARANOIA ANY IF HE KNEW **I** WAS SKIMMING CASH FROM THE STORE HERE AND THERE. THANK GOD HE DOESN'T KNOW AND I'M NOT AS STUPID AS THOSE OTHER GUYS...

BESIDES, THOSE GUYS WERE REALLY FUCKING HIM OVER... I JUST NEED A LITTLE EXTRA CASH FOR BEER AND STUFF...

THE NEXT DAY...

HEY, DID YOU GET ANY NEW UNDERGROUND COMICS? THIS STUFF'S BEEN HERE SINCE I WORKED HERE...

I THINK THERE'S A NEW WEIRDO OVER THERE, BUT WE MIGHT'A SOLD OUT... I'VE BEEN TRYING TO GET A BIG ORDER IN FOR A WHILE BUT DICK KEEPS PUTTING IT OFF...

THAT SUCKS. THIS IS JUST ABOUT THE ONLY PLACE TO GET GOOD COMICS IN TOWN...

I KNOW... BUT YOU KNOW DICK, HE GETS UPTIGHT ABOUT MONEY SOMETIMES... HE'S STILL JUST BARELY SCRAPING BY EVERY MONTH...

MAN, HE'LL **ALWAYS** BE SCRAPING BY... I SEE HE'S STILL LEAVING HIS CIG-ARETTES STANDING ON THE ENDS 'TIL THEY BURN OUT...

YEAH... AND HE LEAVES THEM ALL OVER THE PLACE TOO... IT'S **DISGUSTING!**

LAST YEAR HE LEFT ONE ON A BOOK AND IT CAUGHT ON **FIRE**... IT WAS PRETTY FUNNY... BUT DICK DIDN'T THINK SO...

I'LL BET.

OH MAN, I JUST REMEMBERED A PRETTY FUNNY "DICK" STORY...

LET'S HEAR IT...

"WELL... I GUESS IN THE MID-SEVENTIES DICK USED TO DRIVE UP TO L.A. A FEW TIMES A MONTH TO GET BOOKS AND HE DISCOVERED THIS LITTLE STRIP-JOINT ON THE WAY... AND THERE WAS THIS GIRL WHO WORKED THERE WHO WOULD END HER ACT BY PICKING A GUY OUT OF THE AUDIENCE AND FUCKING HIM ONSTAGE, WHICH IS COMPLETELY ILLEGAL, RIGHT?

51

"SO ANYWAY, DICK STARTS GOING THERE EVERY WEEK HOPING TO GET PICKED... AND SHE FINALLY PICKS HIM..."

"...AND THEY'RE ON STAGE DOIN' IT IN FRONT OF EVERYBODY AND THE **COPS** BUST IN TO CLOSE THE PLACE DOWN..."

EVERYBODY FREEZE!!

"AND DICK JUST MOTIONS TO THE COPS TO WAIT AND THEY STOP AND HE KEEPS FUCKING UNTIL HE CUMS... AND THEN THEY ARREST HIM..."

SQUIRT!

APPARENTLY HE TOLD THE COPS IF HE WAS GONNA GET ARRESTED FOR IT HE WAS SURE AS HELL GONNA **FINISH**!

THAT'S PRETTY WILD, I ALWAYS KNEW HE WAS INTO PORNO BUT I DIDN'T KNOW IT WENT THAT FAR...

HE'S PRETTY INTO PORNO, HUH?

YEAH MAN, I HELPED HIM MOVE A COUPLE YEARS AGO AND HE HAD A WHOLE **BOOKCASE** FULL OF PORN MOVIES...

"HE ALSO HAD A WHOLE BOOKCASE FULL OF GORE MOVIES, I THINK HE'S ACTUALLY MORE INTO THAT STUFF. HE KNOWS THE WHOLE HISTORY OF GORE-EFFECTS AND EVERYTHING...

IT ALL STARTED WITH A FEW GUYS LIKE HERSHEL GORDON LEWIS AND IT MOVED ON TO ITS OWN SUBCULTURE WITH MOVIES LIKE "GORE GORE GIRLS" AND THEN...

UH HUH...

"HE HAD THIS ONE VIDEO OF ALL BEASTIALITY STUFF, TOO. I WATCHED PART OF IT, IT WAS LINDA LOVELACE FUCKING A DOG, WHICH WAS PRETTY DISGUSTING BUT KINDA' FASCINATING AT THE SAME TIME...

OH YEAH!! BABY! ARF!

"YEAH... HE HAD SOME PRETTY OUTRAGEOUS STUFF... PRETTY **STRANGE**..."

8

BUT, Y'KNOW, HE'S HAD AN INTERESTING LIFE IF YOU THINK ABOUT IT, HE'S TRAVELLED AROUND AND KNOWS ABOUT A LOT OF STUFF AND HE'S DONE A LOT... HE'S JUST TIED DOWN TO THIS STORE NOW...

YEAH...MAYBE...BUT HE'S REALLY A JERK NOW... HE'S SO PARANOID THAT EVERYONE'S RIPPING HIM OFF... IT'S FUCKING PATHETIC...

WELL... EVERYBODY **IS** RIPPING HIM OFF.

OH **SHIT**... HERE HE COMES, I DIDN'T THINK HE WAS GONNA COME IN TODAY...

UH OH...

HEY DICK, HOW'S IT GOIN'?

JAMES.

SLAM!

I THINK I BETTER TAKE OFF.

PROBABLY A GOOD IDEA...

TWENTY MINUTES LATER...

TOMMY... I DON'T WANT JAMES HANGIN' AROUND HERE... OKAY?

HUNH... WHY?

I'M **SURE** THAT BASTARD WAS STEALING FROM ME WHEN HE WORKED HERE... I JUST CAN'T PROVE IT. BUT IF I COULD I'D **NAIL** HIS ASS TO THE FUCKING **WALL**!!

9

JESUS... CALM DOWN. HE WASN'T STEALING FROM YOU. HE'S MY BEST FRIEND, I THINK I'D **KNOW** IF HE WERE RIPPING YOU OFF! OKAY?

YEAH...WELL... I STILL DON'T WANT HIM AROUND HERE.

NON-FICTION

WHAT**EVER**...

LATER...

OKAY DICK, I'LL SEEYA' IN A FEW DAYS...

GOODBYE.

I CAN'T BELIEVE THAT FUCKER ACTUALLY STAYED TO WATCH ME CLOSE...HE **NEVER** DOES THAT... I COULDN'T GET **ANYTHING** AT ALL... WHAT AN ASSHOLE!

WHAT AM I **THINKING**?! I'M ACTUALLY MAD AT HIM FOR NOT LETTING ME STEAL HIS **MONEY**... JESUS... I'M A TOTAL JERK...

THAT SAME NIGHT...

HEY, YOU WANNA GET A PIZZA?

SURE...

10

54

SHIT! I SPENT THE LAST OF MY MONEY ON THIS BEER...

THEN I GUESS WE'RE NOT GETTING A PIZZA, 'CUZ I'M NOT PAYING FOR ALL OF IT...

NO...GO AHEAD AND ORDER IT... I'LL GO GET SOME MONEY AT MY WORK...

I DON'T **BELIEVE** YOU...

WHAT?!

WHAT?

IF YOU CAN'T FIGURE IT OUT I'M NOT GONNA TELL YOU...

A FEW MINUTES LATER...

SHIT... I CAN'T BELIEVE I BLEW THE COMBO...AH... HERE WE GO...

CLICK!

NO PROBLEM...

WHAT THE **FUCK** IS **THAT**?

11

IS THAT A **PERSON**? IS IT DICK?!

OH MY **GOD**!! WHAT IF HE NEVER LEFT THE STORE?! HE COULD HAVE JUST PRETENDED TO LEAVE TO TRICK ME! OH SHIT!!

POUND POUND

GOTTA PLAY IT COOL...

DICK? IS THAT YOU? I JUST CAME BACK 'CUZ I... I THOUGHT I...UH... DICK?

JESUS...IT'S JUST HIS **COAT**! GOD...

I'M REALLY GLAD I'VE GOT TOMORROW OFF...

RING RING RING RING

PEN CINEMA

HELLO...

DICK...WHAT? BUT TODAY'S MY DAY OFF... YOU'RE AT THE HOSPITAL?!... WELL, WHAT ABOUT DAVE?... FUCK...YEAH, I GUESS SO... I'LL SEE YA' IN A FEW HOURS...

12

FUCK...

C'MON DICK, WHERE **ARE** YOU?... YOU SAID NOON YOU BASTARD...

THIS SUCKS...

HI... SORRY I'M SO LATE...

WELL, THANK GOD YOU'RE — WHAT HAPPENED TO **YOU**?!

YOU'RE NOT GONNA BELIEVE IT. ... I ALMOST DON'T BELIEVE IT...

I WOKE UP LAST NIGHT AROUND THREE OR SO WITH THESE REAL BAD GAS PAINS... JUST **STABBING** PAINS... SO I GO TO TAKE A SHIT AND I'M SITTING ON THE TOILET SHITTING AND THE PAIN JUST KEEPS GETTING WORSE AND WORSE...

"NEXT THING I KNOW I'M ON THE FLOOR... I MUST HAVE PASSED OUT FROM THE PAIN OR SOMETHING...

"SO I GET UP AND CLEAN MYSELF OFF... BUT I STILL HAVE'TA SHIT... SO I SIT BACK DOWN AND THE PAIN STARTS IN AGAIN...

"...AND I GUESS I PASSED OUT AGAIN... I DON'T KNOW HOW LONG I WAS OUT. I GOT UP AND CLEANED MYSELF OFF AND WENT TO BED... MY LEG FELT KINDA STIFF AT THE TIME, BUT I FIGURED IT WOULD BE OKAY... Y'KNOW?" (13)

...BUT IN THE MORNING I COULD HARDLY WALK! TURNS OUT I NOW HAVE A HAIRLINE FRACTURE IN MY THIGHBONE... I GUESS I MUST HAVE FALLEN A LOT HARDER THAN I THOUGHT...

YEAH... I GUESS SO... JESUS...

THAT NIGHT...

—AND THEN HE WAKES UP ON THE FLOOR **AGAIN!** AND HE FELL SO HARD THAT HE BROKE HIS FUCKING **LEG!!**

HA HA! THAT'S UNBELIEVABLE!

THAT'S **PRETTY** RIDICULOUS...

RIDICULOUS?! IT'S TYPICAL! MAN, DICK'S ONLY GOT ONE TYPE OF LUCK ...BAD!

THE GUY'S A TOTAL LOSER...

HEY MAN, DON'T SAY THAT. DICK'S A GOOD GUY! HE'S JUST HAD A LOT OF BAD SHIT HAPPEN TO HIM...

...I KNOW HE'S KIND OF CRAZY, BUT I REALLY LIKE HIM... IF IT WEREN'T FOR DICK I WOULDN'T KNOW ABOUT BUKOWSKI OR THE BEATS OR EVEN UNDERGROUND COMICS... OR JIM THOMPSON OR...

YEAH, ALL THE **REALLY HIP** SHIT!! HA HA...

UM... OR...

YEAH, YOU REALLY LIKE HIM A **LOT.** THAT'S WHY YOU **STEAL** FROM HIM ALL THE TIME.

CHECK HIM OUT! FOR ONCE HE'S FUCKIN' SPEECHLESS...

14

ZZZZZZ

WHERE THE **FUCK** ?!

SET YOUR CHICKE FREE

AM I IN **DICK'S** HOUSE?

?

BZZT... YEAN, BUT I THOUGHT THAT IF I TORE THIS INTO—

HEY... DICK?

HELLO TOMMY.

—THREE EQUAL PIECES THAT IT WOULD

WHAT ARE YOU WATCHING?

IT'S CALLED "LONELY PLANET BOY" IT'S ABOUT THIS GUY... EVERYONE HE CARES FOR TAKES FROM HIM AND JUST LEAVES...

—ELD INTO A PURE PIECE OF ...WELL, NOT COMPLETELY—

HE DOESN'T HAVE THE COURAGE TO REALLY FOLLOW HIS HEART, SO HE JUST TAKES WHAT COMES HIS WAY... HE DISAPPOINTS ALL THE PEOPLE WHO LOVE HIM AND HE DOESN'T TRY TO STOP THEM WHEN THEY WALK AWAY FROM HIM...HE GROWS OLD ALONE AND HE HATES HIMSELF...

PURE...BUT LIKE MY ENDS

SO IT'S NOT **TOO** SUBTLE...

—AREN'T GOING TO STOP ME, IT WASN'T LIKE THIS...

NO ...IT'S NOT.

15

UH...

IT WAS MORE REAL. AT LEAST IT SEEM... THAT WAY... MAYBE NOT

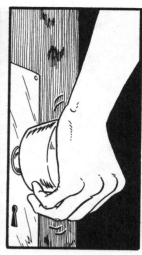

What you all fail to realize about the impact of writers like the Beats and Bukowski is

that no matter how trendy or clichéd they may seem now, they were, at the time they began... a revelation. In both poetry and

DICK, WHO ARE YOU TALKING TO?

prose they communicated exactly what it was to be the first generation of people in America after the Atomic Bomb who were in some way aware that it didn't matter

THERE'S NO ONE HERE ...

anymore... You didn't have to just blindly follow the leader. You could make up your own rules. That the truth of the sadness in your heart was the only really

DICK, STOP IT! NO ONE'S LISTENING!

ZZuhnZZ

16

TWO DAYS LATER...

HEY... IS THAT-?! SHIT, IT **IS**! OH MAN... THIS IS AMAZING...

NEW RELEASES

HEY, SUNNY... WHAT ARE **YOU** DOING HERE?

OH, HI... ACTUALLY I WAS LOOKING FOR YOU, BUT I DIDN'T SEE YOU SO I THOUGHT I'D BROWSE... REMEMBER, YOU TOLD ME YOU WORKED HERE..?

OH, THAT'S RIGHT... WELL, ACTUALLY TODAY'S MY LAST DAY... I'M QUITTING... ONLY MY BOSS DOESN'T KNOW IT YET...

OH REALLY? WELL, ARE YOU GONNA TELL HIM?

YEAH... I **AM**. ANYWAY, I BETTER GET BACK TO WORK, BUT LET ME GET YOUR NUMBER AND I'LL CALL YOU IN A COUPLE DAYS...

OKAY...

MAN... SHE CAME IN LOOKING FOR ME... **COOL**...

NEW RELEA

UH... DICK? I GOTTA TALK TO YOU... IT'S PRETTY IMPORTANT... IF YOU GOT A MINUTE, I MEAN...

FANTASTIC BOO

IT'S... UM... I CAN'T... UHM... I CAN'T WORK HERE ANYMORE... TODAY'S GONNA HAVE TO BE MY LAST DAY... I'VE... UH... I'VE JUST BEEN HERE TOO LONG AND... I... UHM... I...

GRATEFUL

THAT'S FINE, TOMMY, IF THAT'S WHAT YOU WANNA DO... JUST CLOSE UP NOW AND DROP YOUR KEY IN THE MAIL-SLOT. YOU CAN GET PAID IN A FEW DAYS...

UH... OKAY...

17

"THAT'S FINE, TOMMY..."?! THAT'S IT? THAT WAS TOO **EASY**... HE DIDN'T EVEN SEEM TO CARE...

PROBABLY JUST THINKS IT'S JUST ONE MORE FUCKED THING HE'LL HAVE TO DEAL WITH... REPLACING HIS ONLY GOOD EMPLOYEE...

OH **WELL**... WHATEVER...

EPILOG — ABOUT EIGHT MONTHS LATER TOMMY AND HIS FRIEND CHARLIE ARE IN THE STORE LOOKING AROUND...

HEY, I'M GONNA GO SAY HI TO DICK, I HAVEN'T SEEN HIM IN A WHILE... I'LL BE BACK IN A MINUTE...

HUH? OH... SURE.

HEY DICK, HOW'S IT GOING?

HUH?

OH... **YOU**.

YOU WANNA STEP INTO MY OFFICE?

UH...SURE... I **GUESS**...

18

SO...UH... WHAT'S UP?

I JUST WANT YOU TO KNOW THAT YOU'RE NOT SO **SMART**... I DON'T WANT YOU WALKING AROUND ALL SMUG THINKING YOU PUT ONE OVER ON ME...

I'M NOT STUPID. I KNOW WHAT WAS GOING ON THE LAST SIX MONTHS YOU WORKED HERE... ALL THE **VOIDED** SALES... I KNOW YOU WERE **STEALING** THAT MONEY.

UH...LOOK, DICK I—

DON'T **BOTHER** DENYING IT, I'M NOT LOOKING FOR A CONFESSION ... I JUST WANT YOU TO KNOW I **KNOW**... AND I'LL TELL YOU SOMETHING...

I KNEW BACK **THEN**, TOO. THE ONLY REASON I DIDN'T **FIRE** YOU WAS BECAUSE I KNEW YOU WERE GOING THROUGH A HARD TIME AFTER ANNIE LEFT AND I FELT **SORRY** FOR YOU...

MY IN OLD STORE—SEPT '86

IN OLD STORE—SE

"WAITAMINUTE..."

YOU WERE STEALING FROM **HIM**... AND HE FELT SORRY FOR **YOU**..?

YEAH...THAT'S PRETTY MUCH IT...

THAT MAKES **NO** SENSE...HE'S REALLY STRANGE...

19

63

March, 1989...

Where do you think **you're** going ?!

The Problem

Ed Brubaker '93

I'm goin' home, this is ridiculous...

Fine!!

VV-ROOOMM

RING A RING

Hello? Uh... yeah... I think he's asleep, he usually sleeps until at **least** noon... yeah... sure... okay.

DINER

zzz zzz

What are you doin', man?

Watching this fly go around in circles...

65

Any reason?

BZZZZZ ZZZZ

Yeah, I think I've figured out some thing...

Y'see, he's been doing this for at least a half-hour, which has gotta be an insane amount in "fly time"—like a year or something... and I've been watching, thinking, "Don't you know you're going in circles?" But I noticed he doesn't just go in circles, he jumps off to the side and zips back and forth...

...Even though essentially he's going around and around, he flies in an erratic pattern so that he doesn't know he's just going in circles... he might actually think he's making progress...

So I figure he must be a male.

DINER

So, I guess your "big date" last night didn't go too well...

What **date** was that? She didn't even show up...

"I'm sitting there in the restaurant and she's about fifteen minutes late, so I order a beer 'cuz I'm kinda' nervous...so by the time I finish my second beer I figure I've been blown off..."

Turns out she has a **boy friend** and she just felt too bad and couldn't go...

A boyfriend? Why'd she make plans with **you** then?

Who knows? Maybe she was tired of him or something, but then she chickened out... I don't know... but it really bugged me...

2

"After I got off the phone with her I wandered around downtown for about an hour. It was a really beautiful night, but I just couldn't enjoy myself... I just kept thinking about getting stood up... I mean, I hardly knew this girl and it still hurt ... just by asking her out at all I had put myself on the line..."

So I just decided, "Fuck it!" I'm through with relationships, dating, the whole deal...

Yeah, right!

No man, I'm serious... I want out. It never works out anyway... I'm tired of putting myself on the line and I'm tired of wanting to have sex with every attractive woman I meet and I'm **sure** most attractive women are tired of having every guy they meet want to **fuck** them...

You think so? I always figured it'd be easier being an attractive woman...

How?

Well, you could pretty much take your pick of the guys you know, because no guy is gonna turn down sex with a beautiful woman ...So, the way I see it, it's the woman's choice.

That's just what I'm talking about! That's pathetic... that means if you're an attractive girl every male friend you have is just waiting around for his chance. Doesn't that seem fucked up to you?

I never really thought about it much...

Well, I have, and I want no part in this anymore. From now on I'll know people 'cuz I like them as "people"—not 'cuz I wanna stick my dick in them.

Well, have fun getting used to never having sex, smart guy...

Shit, that'll be easy. It's way easier to get used to **not** having sex than it is to get used to having **it**. When you're not having sex, after a few weeks you just settle into it and can just do your own thing...But when you start having sex all the time your whole life changes. You'll do anything to make sure you can keep having sex...you'll blow off all your friends and jump through hoops for some girl who treats you bitchy just so she won't stop spreading her legs for you...

...Like the way you do for Amy now, man...

God, I don't **even** wanna talk about **her** right now.

What, did you guys have **yet** another fight? What about this time?

3

67

Hey, who's Karen?

Huh? She's a girl I met a few weeks ago at Mudd, why?

She called about an hour or so ago... when I first got home.

NER

Jesus, why didn't you **say** something?!

BZZZZZZZZZ
BZZZZ

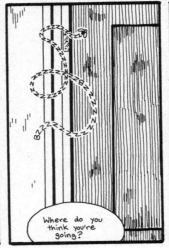

Where do you think you're going?

BZZZZZZZZZZZZZZ THE END

69

JUNE, 1989...

I WAS HAVING THIS RECURRING DREAM...THESE TWO GUYS TORMENTING ME AS I LIE PASSED OUT...

IS HE COHERENT?

NAH... HIS EYES ARE OPEN ...BUT HE'S OUT...

GREAT...YOU GET THE BIBLE...I'LL START CUTTING HIS HAIR...

RROWF GRRRRR

RARWF! ROWF!

JESUS...

THE DOG BARKING WOKE ME UP...IT ALWAYS DID.

THAT FUCKING ANIMAL HATED ME.

MY PLACE

RR RO GGRR

OH GREAT...MY ALARM WASN'T SET. NOW I HAFTA RUSH TO MAKE THE BUS...

FUCK!

THIS SUCKS! IT'S A SHITTY DAY ALREADY...

I HATE THIS STUPID JOB ANYWAY...

BAGGIN' IT

MONDO LOWLIFE

Ed Brubaker '91

71

YOU'RE LATE AGAIN, TOMMY...

YEAH, YEAH...

FUCK OFF DICK!

ACID WASH JEANS

TOMMY?

FINISH UP THAT ORDER ...CLEAN UP... AND COME SEE ME IN TH' OFFICE, OKAY?

SURE...

GREAT... NOW I'LL PROBABLY GET FIRED... SHIT.

MY BOSS RICK WAS A TYRANT. HE LIKED TO WORK US AT AN IMPOSSIBLE PACE BECAUSE HE HAD BEEN THE FASTEST SHIPPER ON EARTH IN HIS DAY...

IS THAT AS FAST AS YOU C'N SHIP? WHEN I WAS A SHIPPER, I SHIPPED $18,000 OF MERCHANDISE IN ONE DAY... AND THEN I FINISHED THE NEXT DAYS...

GOD... WHAT AN ASSHOLE!

HE USED TO BE A RED-NECK HEAVY-METALLER AND HAD WORKED IN THE SHIPPING DEPT. FOR YEARS...

...OYS... TOYS ...OYS... TOYS IN THE ATTIC...

SOMEHOW HE'D BECOME "SHIPPING SUPERVISOR" AND HE LOOKED PRETTY NORMAL NOW ...BUT HE WAS STILL A HEAVY-METAL-RED-NECK AT HEART... I'D ALWAYS FIND HIM ROCKIN' OUT TO SOME SAMMY HAGAR TUNE IN THE OFFICE...

♪ I CAN'T DRIVE FIFTY-FI ♪

...SO HALF AN HOUR LATER I WAS IN HIS OFFICE GETTING A SPEECH...

...YOU'RE JUST NOT WORKIN' FAST ENOUGH AN' YOU'RE GETTIN' AN ATTITUDE TOO... I CAN'T HAVE IT...

I WORK JUST AS FAST AS EVERYONE ELSE!

72

SEE? THERE'S THAT ATTITUDE... YOU THINK YOU'RE BETTER'N EVERY-ONE ELSE HERE... AND NOW YOU'RE COMIN' IN LATE ALL THE TIME...

LIE.

THEY CHANGED THE BUS SCHEDULE !!!

I DON'T CARE. YOU BEEN PUTTIN' IN LESS N' LESS HERE FOR WEEKS.

WHAT DO YOU WANT?... BLOOD!? I PUT IN MY HOURS... FUCK YOU!

I WORK JUST AS HARD AS EVERYBODY ELSE.

YEAH... BUT EVERY-ONE ELSE CARES ABOUT KEEPING THE JOB... YOU GOTTA GET A BETTER ATTITUDE OR YOU'RE OUTTA HERE...

OKAY.

DICK !!

SEE YOU TOMORROW... ON TIME.

I GUESS I WAS STILL MAD ABOUT THE BULLSHIT AT WORK BECAUSE I WASN'T PAYING ATTENTION TO HOW CLOSE I WAS TO THE FENCE...

WHAT AN ASSHOLE... HE DOESN'T KNOW SHIT ABOUT MY LIFE...

GRRRRRRRR RARK!! ROWR! ROWF!

NOT ONLY DID THE DOG HATE ME, BUT HE KNEW I WAS AFRAID OF HIM. SUPPOSEDLY THEY ALWAYS DO...

F! OWF! ARK! ROWF!

AFTER SITTING AROUND THE APART-MENT WATCHING T.V. FOR A WHILE, I DECIDED TO CALL UP SUNNY. I HADN'T TALKED TO HER SINCE WE'D STOPPED SEEING EACH OTHER.

HE WAS ONCE A LITTLE GREEN SLAB OF CLAY...

UNFORTUNATELY, I GOT HER MACHINE...

HI. YOU HAVE REACHED THE HOME OF SUNNY, PAL AND SKEETER... AT THE TONE PLEASE SCREAM AT THE TOP OF YOUR LUNGS AND WE'LL GET BACK TO YOU... ..BEEP!

3

73

JESUS...

I GUESS MY ROOMMATE, JAMES CAME HOME AROUND EIGHT OR SO...

HEY DUMMY!

ZZ*

HUH... WHAT?

I SEE YOU'VE HAD ANOTHER PRODUCTIVE DAY...

WHAT'S THAT SUP-POSED TO MEAN? I WENT TO WORK.

WHAT ABOUT **HERE**? YOU COULD DO THE DISHES OR TAKE OUT THE TRASH...

SO COULD YOU.

IT'S MOSTLY **YOUR** TRASH ANYWAYS... YOUR'S AND AMY'S AND HER SIXTEEN YEAR OLD FRIENDS'...

FUCK YOU.

LOOK **DICK**... I'LL MAKE YOU A DEAL, I'LL DO THE DISHES IF YOU TAKE OUT THE GARBAGE... OKAY?

NO WAY MAN... **IF** I DO ANYTHING, IT'LL BE THE DISHES... BUT EVEN IF I DO THEM, YOU'LL JUST COMPLAIN THAT I DIDN'T DO A GOOD ENOUGH JOB AND RE-DO THEM YOURSELF...

AH... FUCK OFF! YOU'RE UNBELIEVABLE...

WHATEVER...

74

I DECIDED TO GET OUT OF JAMES' WAY FOR A WHILE SO I HEADED DOWN TO SEE FELIX... FELIX IS A REAL INTERESTING CHARACTER... A REALLY CREATIVE GUY WHO IS JUST TOO SCATTERED TO FOCUS IN ANY ONE DIRECTION LONG ENOUGH TO GET ANYTHING DONE...

WHEN I GOT TO HIS PLACE I FOUND HIM SITTING ON THE COUCH IN A TRANCE. HE'D APPARENTLY BEEN UP FOR THREE DAYS...

FELIX? HEY!

HE REVIVED AND WE SAT AROUND DRINKING BEER WHILE FELIX TOLD THE STORY OF THE LAST TWO WEEKS...

YOU REMEMBER THAT GIRL TANYA THAT WAS LIVING WITH ALLEGRO UPSTAIRS? ...

WELL, HE MOVED TO SAN FRANCISCO AND I CAME HOME FROM WORK AND FOUND HER HANGIN' OUT ON THE PORCH... SO SHE MOVED IN FOR A COUPLE DAYS AND AFTER A DAY OR SO WE END UP SLEEPING TOGETHER... SO THEN I HAD TO TELL RHONDA...

I BET SHE WAS PISSED...

SURPRISINGLY, NO! SHE DIDN'T CARE... SHE SAID SHE UNDERSTOOD... AND THEN SHE FLEW DOWN FOR A VISIT AND... UH... NEXT THING YOU KNOW, WE'RE ALL SLEEPING TOGETHER, IT WAS GREAT! ON RHONDA'S LAST NIGHT HERE I HAD TO STRUGGLE TO BE IN THE MIDDLE... BUT AS I WAS LYING THERE, I REALISED THAT THIS WAS WHAT I WANTED FROM MY LIFE...

TO BE SLEEPING WITH TWO GIRLS?!

YEAH...

TWO GIRLS... JESUS... I WISH I COULD EVEN GET IT TOGETHER WITH ONE... WHAT HAPPENED WITH SUNNY? LAST TIME I SAW YOU, YOU WERE TAKING MY BIKE TO GO RIDING WITH HER...

YEAH... WELL, WE SPENT A FEW DAYS TOGETHER AFTER THAT... BUT SHE SAYS I WANT MORE THAN SHE CAN GIVE RIGHT NOW... AND SHE'S PROBABLY RIGHT...

WELL FUCK! YOU SHOULD JUST TAKE WHATEVER YOU CAN GET AND NOT THINK ABOUT COMMITMENT OR THE FUTURE... YOU JUST FUCK IT UP THAT WAY...

YEAH, I KNOW... BUT I CAN'T HELP IT... I'M IN LOVE WITH HER.

5

ON THE WAY HOME I STOPPED AT THE 7-11 TO GET SOME MORE BEER... BUT AS I ENTERED THE ALLEY... SOMETHING WAS NOT RIGHT...

THE DOG HAD GOTTEN OUT SOMEHOW...

GRRRRR...

OH GOD...

ROWR !!! RARK !!! ROWR!

POOSH!

GOD... MY LIFE IS SHIT...

6

76

77

AS I STOOD IN THE KITCHEN DRINKING WATER BY THE JUGFUL I HEARD A STRANGE SOUND...

...LIKE WIND CRACKLING THROUGH THE TRASH... BUT THE WINDOW WAS CLOSED...

I LOOKED REAL CLOSE... AND I SAW IT...

THE TRASH WAS COMPLETELY COVERED WITH MAGGOTS... THE CRACKLING SOUND WAS THEIR CRAWLING ON THE PLASTIC... MY STOMACH TURNED...

GEE... I HOPE JAMES TAKES OUT THAT TRASH SOON...

ROWF!!

RARK!! ROWF!!

THE END

78

I'M KINDA' PISSED AT MY FRIEND FELIX RIGHT NOW... AS PISSED AS ANYONE CAN EVER BE AT HIM...HE'S JUST THE KINDA' GUY YOU CAN'T STAY TOO MAD AT—HE'D NEVER DO ANYTHING TO INTENTIONALLY HURT YOU...

...HE'S JUST A FLAKE... A DISAPPOINTMENT.

AND I GUESS I SYMPATHIZE WITH THIS BECAUSE I KNOW I'VE BEEN A DISAPPOINTMENT A LOT OF THE TIME, TOO, JUST LIKE HIM...SO IT'S HARD FOR ME TO STAY MAD. AND BESIDES THAT THERE'S JUST SOMETHING KIND OF INFECTIOUS ABOUT THE GUY, AND I THINK ANYONE WHO KNOWS HIM'D TELL YOU THE SAME THING, WHETHER THEY'RE MAD AT HIM OR NOT. SEE, FELIX LIVES LIFE DIFFERENTLY THAN MOST PEOPLE, OR AT LEAST THAT'S HOW IT USED TO SEEM TO ME...BUT I'M GETTING AHEAD OF MYSELF HERE, AND I SHOULDN'T DO THAT BECAUSE I WANT YOU TO REALLY UNDERSTAND THIS...

I FIRST MET FELIX IN 1987 AT THE BOOKSTORE WHERE I WORKED AND WE BECAME FRIENDS OVER THE NEXT FEW MONTHS. HE WAS ABOUT THE MOST ENERGETIC GUY I'D MET SINCE I QUIT DOING SPEED...

Well, if you like old country music then you've gotta check out Gram Parsons, he's just essential listening... Way ahead of his time...

Graham Parker?

SOMEHOW WE DECIDED TO START A BAND AND ABOUT ONCE A WEEK WE'D GET TOGETHER AND DRINK AND PLAY SONGS. I THINK WE WERE SERIOUS FOR TWO OR THREE WEEKS...

ALL THESE CRAZY MIXED-UP LIES--

OF COURSE SOME OF FELIX' ENERGY CAME FROM THE FACT THAT HE REALLY WAS A PRETTY BIG SPEED FREAK AT THE TIME—HE WAS ALWAYS RACING OFF TO THE BATHROOM AND COMING BACK RARIN' TO GO...

TO BE HONEST, AT THE TIME I DIDN'T SUSPECT A THING. I WAS SUFFERING PRETTY BADLY OVER BREAKING-UP WITH MY GIRLFRIEND AND FELIX WAS SIMPLY A GREAT PERSON TO BE AROUND WHEN YOU WERE IN PAIN.

You may not believe this now, but there will be other women ...they'll destroy you just like this, but they'll be there...

No man... not like this...

HE REALLY UNDERSTOOD PAIN AND WE HAD LONG DISCUSSIONS ABOUT LIFE AND LOVE AND HE HELPED ME TO UNDERSTAND A BIT...

Worse than this, believe me. That's just the way life works... every time I've ever thought I'd never be in love again —BANG! It happens... Worse than ever.

FELIX ON PAIN:

My philosophy is give yourself freely to your pain and suffering, they're part of life, you've gotta savor every part of life... there'll be a day in the future when you'll look at this as a good time — because the pain made it more important...

PERSONALLY, I'M MORE THE TYPE TO TRY AND RUN FROM PAIN AND SUFFERING...

1

ONE OF THE FIRST THINGS THAT JUMPED OUT AT ME ABOUT FELIX WAS HIS OBSESSIONS WITH CERTAIN WOMEN. HE WAS ALWAYS FINDING A NEW GIRL TO BE "INTO", EVEN WHEN HE HAD A GIRLFRIEND. HE'D SPOT ONE IN A STORE AND THE NEXT THING YOU KNOW, HE'S A REGULAR SHOPPER THERE.

That girl behind the counter... GASP! She's a goddess!

Oh man, you've gotta see this girl at the 7-11 in El Cabrillo... She's amazing...

EL CABRILLO?! That's fifteen miles away! You drive fifteen miles to go to a 7-11?

I know, but she's HOT! I'm "into" her...

WHILE I COULD CERTAINLY UNDERSTAND THIS, I COULDN'T BELIEVE HOW OFTEN THE GIRLS WERE INTERESTED IN HIM, TOO. IN FACT, IT SOON BECAME CLEAR TO ME THAT ALMOST ALL GIRLS WERE INTERESTED IN HIM. HE ALWAYS HAS SOMETHING TO TALK TO THEM ABOUT AND HE SEEMS REALLY SELF-ASSURED. BUT IT'S MORE THAN THAT... THERE'S A SORT OF "FELIX-APPEAL" AND GUYS FALL VICTIM TO IT TOO, IT'S JUST WORSE WITH GIRLS...

I SAY THIS BECAUSE, OF COURSE, I'M JEALOUS OF HIM... HE'S GOT SOMETHING I JUST DON'T HAVE... THAT CHARM, THAT CONFIDENCE.

What's your friend's name?

I don't min... hard, but I'll tell you how I feel... I wa

HE'S THE ULTIMATE INSIDER. WHOEVER HE'S TALKING TO, HE FINDS A COMMON GROUND WITH THEM. HE'S ALWAYS REACHING OUT, WANTING TO MEET NEW PEOPLE, WANTING TO TALK... AND EVERYBODY LIKES HIM. IF SOMEONE WERE MAKING A MOVIE OF OUR LIVES, HE'D DEFINITELY BE THE STAR AND I'D BE THE SIDEKICK...

Tommy, you're not in this shot. This is the one where the girl makes the play for FELIX!

HELL, EVEN WHEN I WAS IN A PUNK BAND IN HIGH SCHOOL I NEVER FELT LIKE AN INSIDER, I FELT LIKE I COULDN'T EVEN IDENTIFY WITH MY OWN CROWD MOST OF THE TIME AND THAT REALLY CONFUSED ME.

I GOT THE WORLD UP MY ASS AN' I'M GONN

TSOL
Abolish Government

BUT FELIX, IF HE WERE THERE HE'D HAVE BASKED IN IT, HE IDENTIFIES WITH EVERYBODY... AND I'M JEALOUS OF THAT BECAUSE THAT CONFUSED FEELING IS SOMETHING I'VE CONTINUED TO CARRY WITH ME AS I'VE GROWN UP—AN ISOLATION.

2

WHICH, I GUESS IS ONE OF THE REASONS I'M PISSED AT FELIX RIGHT NOW, BECAUSE HE'S ONE OF THE FEW PEOPLE WHO REALLY SEEM TO KNOW ME, AND WHEN I TALK TO HIM I NEVER WORRY THAT HE WON'T UNDER — STAND ME — WE CUT RIGHT THROUGH TO THE HEART.

ANOTHER THING I'M JEALOUS OF FELIX FOR IS HIS ABILITY TO GET AWAY WITH EVERYTHING... ONE TIME HIS GIRLFRIEND WAS OUT OF TOWN AND HE AND I WENT OUT DRINKING AND THIS GIRL WE KNEW WAS COMING ON TO FELIX PRETTY HARD...

WE WERE GETTING PRETTY DRUNK, BUT IT SEEMED LIKE HE WAS GOING TO DO THE RIGHT THING AND BRUSH HER OFF, THEN ON THE WAY HOME IT OCCURS TO HIM ...

Here's this girl — who's beautiful, right? — and she wants me... So what's the harm? I'd want Rhonda to do the same thing...

SO I DROP HIM OFF AT HER PLACE AND HE BUZZES HER APARTMENT.

BZZT!

SHE DOESN'T ANSWER THOUGH, BECAUSE SHE'S PASSED-OUT DRUNK.

FELIX WASN'T GONNA GIVE UP THAT EASY NOW THAT HE WAS HERE, SO HE DECIDES TO CLIMB UP THE DRAIN-PIPE TO HER WINDOW — FIGURING THAT IF HE CAN GET IN HER WIN-DOW, HE CAN GET LAID.

SHE LIVED ON THE FOURTH FLOOR, BUT HE ONLY GOT TO THE THIRD...

HE LAID ON THE GROUND OUTSIDE HER WINDOW FOR EIGHT HOURS BEFORE SOMEONE CALLED AN AMBULANCE. HE'D BROKEN HIS LEGS AND SOME RIBS, BUT NOTHING ELSE. AND WHEN HIS GIRLFRIEND CAME HOME HE JUST TOLD HER HE WAS DRUNK AND DIDN'T RE-MEMBER ANYTHING... AND THEN SHE TOOK CARE OF HIM FOR THE NEXT TWO MONTHS. I COULDN'T BELIEVE IT...

③

ANOTHER TIME HE WAS DRUNK AT A SHOW AND STARTED MAKING-OUT WITH HIS FRIEND PAT'S GIRLFRIEND RIGHT IN FRONT OF EVERYBODY... PAT INCLUDED...

What the FUCK?!

PAT YANKS HER HAIR AND RUNS OUTSIDE. THEY FOLLOW HIM AND WHILE SHE'S TRYING TO CALM PAT DOWN, FELIX BUTTS IN TO TRY AND HELP... LISTEN TO THIS ONE:

Pat, man... there's no reason to be mad ... we're just "people."

WHEN HE TOLD ME THAT, I LAUGHED...

I can't believe you... Man, if you'd've made-out with Sunny, I'd've beat the crap out of you. Especially if you said that to me...

WELL, TWO WEEKS LATER HE ACTUALLY DOES KISS SUNNY, WHILE I'M NO LESS THAN TWENTY FEET AWAY. SHE TOLD ME ABOUT IT THE NEXT NIGHT BECAUSE SHE FEELS GUILTY AND BECAUSE SHE DOESN'T WANT ME TO FIND OUT FROM HIM.

WHEN I CONFRONT FELIX LATER HE'S UNCERTAIN FOR A SECOND IF I'M GOING TO HIT HIM...

Well, I figured she'd tell you... but I thought later, not right away... Certainly not the next day...

BUT, SOMEHOW IT'S NOTHING WORTH HITTING A FRIEND OVER. SURE, IT HURTS, BUT TO BE MAD AT HIM I'D HAVE TO BE MAD AT HER, TOO... AND I AM, BUT I LOVE HER AND SHE WAS JUST CURIOUS, AND IN ALL HONESTY, WE REALLY ARE JUST PEOPLE.

THAT'S WHAT GETS ME ABOUT HIM, HE'S ACTUALLY RIGHT ABOUT THIS STUFF IN A LOT OF WAYS. HE'S COMING AT LIFE FROM AN ENTIRELY DIFFERENT PERSPECTIVE THAN ME... I KNOW THAT OFTEN HE DOESN'T THINK OF THE CONSEQUENCES OF HIS ACTIONS AND HE THRIVES ON CHAOS, BUT SOMEWHERE IN THERE HE KNOWS SOMETHING MOST PEOPLE DON'T.

WHEN I LOOK AT HIM AND SUNNY I THINK THAT THEY BOTH ARE REALLY ALIVE, THEY BOTH SHOW ME SOMETHING I DON'T GET ON MY OWN. THEY HAVE AN ENERGY AND A HOPEFULNESS THAT I'LL NEVER COME CLOSE TO AND I FEEL MORE ALIVE AROUND THEM... MORE ENGAGED... WHICH IS WHY I LOVE THEM BOTH SO MUCH.

4

THE LAST TIME I SAW FELIX WAS WHEN I WAS VISITING SUNNY FOR HER BIRTHDAY... WE ALL GOT TOGETHER TO TIE-ONE-ON, AS USUAL...

I REMEMBERED ALL THE GREAT TIMES I'D HAD WITH THEM BOTH, AND CRAZY TIMES TOO... LIKE BEING AT THE ZOO WITH FELIX ON ACID AND HAVING A HUGE DISCUSSION ABOUT EVERYTHING IN FRONT OF THE GORILLA PEN...

won't be people in my universe, just big peering bears, puppy dog eyes, rainbow blossoms, having to pee pine cones an—

—but nothing is just in the eyes of other nothings. Ultimately being nothing, but the way the universe masturbates is not bad—

AND I REMEMBERED REALLY BAD TIMES IN MAYNARDVILLE IN 1988 AND '89, WALKING THE STREETS LATE AT NIGHT WHEN I COULDN'T SLEEP AND I'D LOOK DOWN FELIX' ALLEY AND IF THE KITCHEN LIGHT WAS ON, NO MATTER WHAT TIME IT WAS, I KNEW SHELTER WAS INSIDE FOR THE ASKING.

THAT LAST NIGHT TOGETHER WE WENT FOR MORE BEER AND THE OLD LADY AT THE STORE TRIED TO HELP US AND WE EXPLAINED TO HER THAT OUR GIRLFRIENDS HAD GIVEN US MONEY AND SHE LAUGHED AND SAID:

Ain't that the way of it... Heh heh...

AND THEN IT HIT ME... NO, THAT WASN'T THE WAY OF IT. SHE WASN'T MY GIRLFRIEND ANYMORE AND THIS WASN'T MY LIFE ANYMORE AND I MISSED IT ALL SO MUCH.

IT'S SUCH A BITTERSWEET THING TO BE IN THE ROOM WITH SOMEONE YOU LOVE WHEN YOU'RE LEAVING IN TWO DAYS AND IT'S OVER BETWEEN YOU... I BREAK DOWN IN TEARS IN SUNNY'S LAP KNOWING IT'S JUST MORE PROOF OF MY WEAKNESS...

Shhh... It's okay, baby... Shhh...

BUT IT'S NOT JUST HER, IT'S HIM TOO... WATCHING HOW HE'D CHANGED—OR STOPPED CHANGING. HE'S ALWAYS BEEN SO SCATTERED THAT HE COULDN'T GET ANYTHING DONE... BUT HE'D ALWAYS **LIVED** IN SO MANY DIFFERENT WAYS...

5

BUT HERE HE WAS, STUCK IN EVERYTHING HE'D FEARED THE MOST... HE WAS LIVING WITH HIS GIRLFRIEND, WORKING A FULL-TIME JOB IN A WAREHOUSE AND HE WAS DYING.

IT WAS DRAGGING HIM DOWN, HE WASN'T RETURNING PHONE CALLS OR GOING OUT. HE WAS JUST WORKING, COMING HOME AND DRINKING IN FRONT OF THE T.V., HE HAD LET IT ALL GET TO HIM.

AND I THOUGHT ABOUT MY FRIEND HART DOWN IN MEXICO, LIVING HIS FANTASY, GETTING "FREE" FOR THE FIRST TIME, SENDING ME CRAZY CARDS ABOUT DRUNKEN ESCAPADES AND FALLING IN LOVE WITH EVERY GIRL HE MEETS AND IT REMINDS ME OF FELIX...

...THE WAY HE USED TO BE. AND I THINK OF HIM NOW, IN HIS JOB, HIS CLUTTERED LITTLE APARTMENT, AND HIS DEADEND, JUST LOOKING AT ME AND SAYING, "I've gotta get away from all this."

BUT HE'S BEEN SAYING THAT FOR YEARS NOW AND I GUESS THAT'S PART OF WHY I'M PISSED.

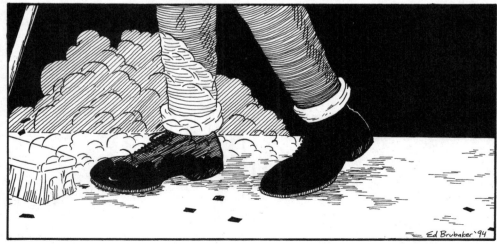

Ed Brubaker '94

84

the Other Shoe

BILLY BUTLER, WHO'S NEVER BEEN KNOWN FOR HIS EMOTIONAL OUTBURSTS, INFORMED ME THE OTHER DAY THAT—

LIFE IS FILLED WITH IMMENSE SADNESS.

WHICH OF COURSE GOT ME THINKING OF SUNNY, YET AGAIN...

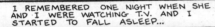

I REMEMBERED ONE NIGHT WHEN SHE AND I WERE WATCHING T.V. AND I STARTED TO FALL ASLEEP...

SUNNY POKED ME... AND SAID "YOU'RE SLEEPING" AND SMILED, AND I FELT AS IF I WERE COMING OUT OF A DREAM AND SHE WASN'T REALLY THERE.

I HAD THIS SUDDEN REALIZATION OF HOW BEAUTIFUL SHE WAS AND HOW MUCH I LOVED HER AND HOW BADLY I'D MISS HER WHEN IT WAS ALL OVER...

IT WAS A SILENT LITTLE MOMENT OF TRUTH AND IT SCARED THE HELL OUT OF ME.

THE FALL OF 1991...

JESUS CHRIST, CAN'T I EVEN GO TO THE BATHROOM BY MYSELF?!

STOMP STON STO

I HAD'TA GO, TOO...

WAKE UP SWEETIE... I MADE YOU ♪ COFFEE... ♪♫

IS HELL

I'M REALLY SORRY I WAS SUCH A BITCH LAST NIGHT. I DIDN'T MEAN TO GET IN A FIGHT... I JUST GET SO CRAMPED SOMETIMES...

GOD... I'M JUST SORRY ... THAT'S ALL.

YEAH... ME TOO.

NOW, IF YOU HURRY UP AND GET DRESSED YOU CAN WALK ME TO WORK.

"IT WAS JUST THE WAY IT WAS SUPPOSED TO BE... THE LIGHT OF A NEW DAY MAKING ALL YOUR TROUBLES LOOK SMALLER...

3

"WE HAD A NICE LITTLE MORNING WALK, TALKING ABOUT MAYBE GOING TO VISIT MY DAD IN SANTA FE..."

"EVERYTHING WAS GOING GREAT, THEN I LEAN OVER TO KISS HER GOODBYE AND WHEN I START TO OPEN MY MOUTH... SHE PULLS AWAY."

...I JUST DON'T WANT YOU TO KISS ME THAT WAY RIGHT NOW...

JESUS, I FELT THAT ONE RIGHT IN MY STOMACH... I DIDN'T KNOW WHAT TO THINK. I STILL DON'T...

I'M TELLING YOU MAN, IT'S "LIVING TOGETHER."

PEOPLE SHOULDN'T DO IT, IT RUINS THINGS. YOU GET TIRED OF SOMEONE IF YOU HAVE TO SEE THEM EVERYDAY... AND THEY GET TIRED OF YOU, TOO.

WHAT'RE YOU TALKIN' ABOUT? YOU'RE LIVIN' WITH FRANNIE NOW, AND YOU WERE LIVIN' WITH RHONDA FOR YEARS BEFORE THAT!

YEAH, I KNOW AND YOU'D THINK I'D KNOW BETTER BY NOW...

BUT I'M SERIOUS MAN, "FAMILIARITY BREEDS CONTEMPT," IT'S TRUE.

YEAH, AND "A PROPHET IS NEVER RECOGNISED IN HIS OWN COUNTRY."

UH... HOW DOES THAT ONE CORRESPOND TO THIS SITUATION?

④

WELL, LIKE WHEN YOU'RE WITH SOMEONE, AND YOU'RE AROUND THEM ALL THE TIME... THEN THEY CAN'T SEE HOW GREAT YOU REALLY ARE...

YEAH, THAT'S WHAT I SAID, "FAMILIARITY BREEDS CONTEMPT."

WHATEVER... I LIKE MINE...

SURE YOU DO, IN YOURS, YOU'RE A "PROPHET"...

WHAT IS IT?! WHAT'S WRONG?

SNIFF... I DON'T KNOW... SOB... I DON'T KNOW...

JESUS... WHAT AM I GONNA DO?

...I SWEAR TO GOD IF JOE EVER LOOKS AT ME LIKE THAT AGAIN I'M GONNA FILE FUCKING CHARGES.

YEAH, HE'S A REAL CREEP THE WAY HE DROOLS OVER YOU GIRLS... MAKES ME GLAD I'M A GUY.

5

WELL, HERE COMES YOUR BOY-FRIEND... I'LL SEEYA TOMORROW...

ELMHURST NATURAL FOOD

WHAT THE FUCK?! WHY'S HE TAKING OFF RIGHT AS I GET HERE?

HI...

HI.

WHAT'S GOIN' ON WITH BILL? WHY'D HE TAKE OFF LIKE THAT WHEN HE SAW ME COMIN'?

NOTHING'S GOING ON, HE JUST HAD TO GO BACK TO WORK. WE WERE JUST HAVING A SMOKE...

Y'KNOW WHAT I DON'T GET? YOU WORK AT A HEALTH FOOD STORE, YOU WON'T EAT MEAT OR CHICKEN, YOU EXERCISE, USE NATURAL REMEDIES AND ALL THAT KINDA' SHIT... AND EVERYONE YOU WORK WITH IS THE SAME WAY...

...AND YOU ALL SMOKE!

I MEAN, WHAT'S THE DEAL? IF YOU CARE SO MUCH ABOUT BEING HEALTHY, WHY'RE YOU SMOKING? HAVE ANY OF YOU EVER HEARD OF CANCER? BECAUSE, YOU KNOW, THEY SAY THAT <u>SMOKING</u> CAUSES IT...

WHY NOT JUST EAT STEAK, TOO? OR IS THIS SOME KIND OF "LOVE-HATE" RELATION-SHIP WITH YOUR OWN BODY?

FUCK YOU. YOU'RE JUST JEALOUS 'CUZ YOU SAW ME SITTING WITH BILL. YOU'RE SO TRANS-PARENT.

6

YOU'RE JUST MAD BECAUSE I'M RIGHT.

I'M MAD BECAUSE YOU'RE AN ASSHOLE.

THIS IS THE BEST DEPRESSED SONG *EVER*, MAN... I'M TELLING YOU... HANDS DOWN...

WHAT IS IT?

JUST WAITAMINUTE... YOU'LL SEE...

♫ ...WHY'D YOU DO THIS TO ME..? ♫ SHOWIN' ME THAT ALL I'M GOOD FOR... IS TO WATCH YOU SLEEP... AS LIFELESS AS AN ANGEL...

OH CHRIST, NOT THIS SONG AGAIN! HE'S ALWAYS TRYING TO SHOVE SOME NEW "GREAT" SONG DOWN EVERYBODY'S THROAT...

WHAT?! WHAT'S WRONG WITH THIS SONG? IT *IS* GREAT!

7

I DON'T KNOW, MAN, SOUNDS KINDA' OVERPRODUCED...

♪ WHY WON'T YOU STAY? WHY WON'T YOU STAY..? ♪

LISTEN TO THE WORDS! FUCK THE PRODUCTION!

I CAN'T JUST LISTEN TO THE WORDS, LYRICS AREN'T THAT IMPORTANT TO ME...

JESUS, YOU GUYS'LL ARGUE ABOUT ANYTHING.

FUCK THAT. WORDS ARE IMPORTANT... FUCK ALL YOUR "BUTTHOLE SURFERS" SHIT...

—WAIT, STOP... I CAN'T... I DON'T—

WHAT?! BUT I THOUGHT...

8

92

I JUST DON'T FEEL LIKE IT...

WELL, WHEN **ARE** YOU GONNA FEEL LIKE IT? IT'S BEEN ALMOST THREE MONTHS...

I DON'T KNOW...

HI, I BROUGHT STUFF HOME FOR DINNER.

OH, GREAT...

GODDAMN IT TOMMY!!

YOU DIDN'T DO THE DISHES.

OH SHIT, SORRY. I JUST GOT ALL WRAPPED UP IN THIS BOOK...

IT'S ALWAYS ONE EXCUSE OR ANOTHER.

WHAT'S **THAT** SUPPOSED TO MEAN?

I MEAN YOU DON'T DO ANYTHING AROUND HERE!! ALL YOU DO IS SIT AROUND AND READ OR WATCH T.V!!

THAT'S TOTAL BULLSHIT!! I DO THE DISHES ALMOST EVERY DAY!!!

YOU DO NOT!!

I DO TOO!!

"OUR FIGHTS ALWAYS ESCALATE INTO A REAL PRIMAL YOU-VERSUS-ME KINDA' THING..."

SOMETIMES I FEEL LIKE WE JUST PUT SO MUCH STOCK IN EACH OTHER EARLY ON, THAT **ANY** DISAGREEMENT NOW IS LIKE A BETRAYAL... WE'RE MAD AT EACH OTHER FOR NOT BEING PERFECT...

AND WE USED TO GET ALONG SO GREAT, TOO. NOW IT SEEMS LIKE THE SLIGHTEST LITTLE THING'LL SET US OFF AND ALL OF A SUDDEN WE'RE SCREAMIN' AT EACH OTHER.

YEAH, THAT'S A DRAG, MAN...

10

Y'KNOW, I'M SO AFRAID OF LOSING HER, AND YET I'M WATCHING IT HAPPEN AND THERE'S NOTHING I CAN DO...

OH C'MON, YOU'RE NOT "LOSING HER", YOU GUYS JUST NEED TO GIVE EACH OTHER SOME SPACE...

NO MAN, YOU'RE WRONG... I LIVE IN CONSTANT FEAR THAT TONIGHT WILL BE THE LAST NIGHT I SPEND WITH HER... EVERY NIGHT...

YOU DON'T LIVE IN CONSTANT FEAR, YOU LIVE IN CONSTANT MELO- DRAMA, THAT'S ALL...

AND OUR LANDLADY LEFT US A NOTE ABOUT OUR YELLING... FUCKIN' BITCH... SHE'LL PROB- ABLY KICK US OUT ANY DAY NOW...

HEY MAN, CHECK OUT THIS NEW "SISTER PILOTS" LP I PICKED UP—

SO, WHAT DO YOU WANNA DO?

I DON'T KNOW. OUR LEASE IS COMING UP IN A FEW MONTHS...

11

95

...MAYBE WE SHOULD MOVE OUT. I MEAN, PART OF OUR PROBLEM RIGHT NOW IS THAT THAT PLACE IS JUST TOO DAMN SMALL ... WE'RE DRIVING EACH OTHER CRAZY.

YEAH, IT IS A PRETTY SMALL PLACE FOR TWO PEOPLE...

SO, DO YOU WANNA TRY TO GET A BIGGER PLACE, OR DO YOU WANNA NOT LIVE TOGETHER ANYMORE?

I DON'T KNOW... I GUESS WE SHOULD TRY NOT LIVING TOGETHER FOR A WHILE. JUST TO SEE HOW IT FEELS.

SORT OF LIKE A "TRIAL SEPARATION" LIKE MARRIED COUPLES DO?

I GUESS SO...

SOMETIMES I FEEL LIKE WE'RE CHAINED TOGETHER... LIKE THE IDEA OF LIVING WITHOUT EACH OTHER IS JUST **NOT** AN OPTION ANYMORE.

AND I DON'T EVEN **KNOW** IF I WANT TO BE WITHOUT YOU,... I DON'T EVEN HAVE ENOUGH OF MYSELF ANYMORE TO KNOW THAT... SOMETIMES I WISH...

...I WISH ONE OF US WOULD DIE, SO THAT THE OTHER COULD BE FREE. THAT'D BE EASIER THAN BREAKING UP. BUT THEN, IF IT WAS **YOU** WHO DIED, I'D MISS YOU...

12

STOP LOOKING AT ME LIKE THAT.

WE'RE NEVER GONNA HAVE SEX AGAIN, ARE WE?

I DON'T KNOW... I CAN'T SAY FOR **SURE** THAT WE AREN'T... I JUST DON'T WANNA GO ON HAVING IT AS IF NOTHING WAS WRONG... THAT'S ALL...

WELL IT'S NOT MAKING IT ANY BETTER AS FAR AS I'M CONCERNED... MAYBE IF I FELT LIKE YOU WERE ATTRACTED TO ME I'D BE—

13

You have to realize that it wasn't always like this, that this is the portrait of a dead horse being kicked... But there was a time not too long before when it was like magic, a time of running in the rain, and making love everywhere and endless postcards filled with passion and tears... That must be remembered...

15

JESUS...

I HATE THAT LADDER, Y'KNOW IT— IT STICKS RIGHT OUT OVER THE STREET INSTEAD OF OVER THE FIRE ESCAPE...FUCK, ONE MISSED RUNG AND THAT'S IT... STREET PIZZA.

...IT'S CRAZY... I'VE SEEN THREE HOUSES JUST EXPLODE...

AS NIGHT FELL WE COULD ONLY SEE THE HOUSES THAT WERE ON FIRE, THEY SHIMMERED LIKE LITTLE FIREFLIES FOR A MOMENT OR TWO BEFORE THE FLAMES GOT TO THEIR GAS LINES AND THEN THEY DISAPPEARED IN A FLASH.

—THE AREAS FROM ROCKRIDGE TO ASHBY ARE BEING TOLD TO PREPARE FOR EVACUATION. THE FIRE STILL —

...YEAH... YOU ARE?... JESUS...

...YEAH, WE'RE GETTIN' READY. I DON'T THINK IT'LL GET THIS FAR, BUT JUST IN CASE...

I'M GONNA STAY UP ALL NIGHT TO KEEP A LOOK- OUT...

YEAH... OKAY... GOOD LUCK.

WELL, RICHARD'S PACKING UP HIS CAR AND THEY'RE GONNA STAY AT A FRIEND'S. HE THINKS THEIR PLACE'LL BURN, PROBABLY...

THAT SUCKS.

16

100

ARE YOU REALLY SURE YOU WANNA STAY UP?

YEAH, I'D BE TOO PARANOID TO SLEEP ANYWAY, I'M SURE...

MY HERO.

WELL, WAKE ME UP IF THE BUILDING BURNS DOWN, OKAY?

WILL DO.

—RIGHT NOW FIRE-FIGHTERS STILL DON'T HAVE THE BLAZE UNDER CONTROL... WE—

GOD, WHAT ARE WE GONNA DO?... FUCK.

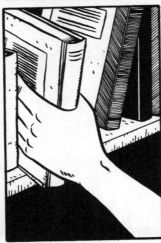

WHAT?

(17)

101

T- Decided to take BART instead of Bus. Going to go thriftshopping.

I know it's stupid, but I can't get Andre's death out of my mind. I keep thinking, what if I'd come home and found _you_ dead? What would I do? I'd be all alone.

Life is just a bunch of lines, thin ones, connecting people and places.

Sunny —————— Tommy
I love you —S

WAKE UP, HONEY... WAKE UP...

-HUH?

YOU FELL ASLEEP... C'MON, LET'S GO TO BED...

I LOVE YOU...

18

102

MEMORY IS A FUNNY THING. RECENTLY I READ A BOOK THAT SAID MEMORY IS ACTUALLY A PLACE — WHEN YOU WALK BY A PLACE IT CAN REMIND YOU OF A PERSON, OR OF A THING THAT HAPPENED TO YOU THERE. THAT'S SORT OF HOW SUNNY THOUGHT.

TO ME IT'S ALSO LIKE A MAZE, WITH ONE MEMORY SENDING YOU CAREENING AROUND A CORNER INTO ANOTHER, UNTIL YOU'RE HOPELESSLY LOST.

WHICH EXPLAINS WHY I HAD TO LEAVE THE BAY AREA. THE WHOLE TIME I'D LIVED THERE I WAS WITH SUNNY.

THERE WASN'T ONE LAMP-POST I COULDN'T SEE US KISSING UNDER, NOT ONE RESTAURANT I COULD EAT IN WITHOUT REMEMBERING A BETTER TIME THERE WITH HER.

NOT ONE DAY WENT BY THAT I DIDN'T FIND MYSELF EXPECTING TO SEE HER EVERYWHERE, BECAUSE I DID SEE HER EVERYWHERE IN MY MIND. NOW, YEARS LATER, MY MEMORY IS STILL UNCOMFORTABLY SHARP, AND I STILL STUMBLE INTO THE MAZE WHEN I THINK OF HER.

ONE THOUGHT WILL BE OF HOW NICE IT WOULD BE JUST TO HOLD HER FOR A MOMENT, AND THAT'LL REMIND ME OF SOME STUBBORN FIGHT WE HAD, WHICH WILL SEND ME INTO THE FEAR I FELT SO OFTEN OF LOSING HER, AND THEN I'LL TURN THE CORNER INTO HER SMILE AND THE WAY SHE MOVED.

I FIND MYSELF TRYING TO FIGURE OUT HOW WE GOT SO STUCK. WAS IT REALLY JUST LITTLE FEARS THAT GOT ESCALATED, OR WAS IT SOMETHING MORE FUNDAMENTAL?

I THINK PEOPLE GET HUNG UP ON THE LITTLE PROBLEMS OF DAY-TO-DAY LIFE AND LOSE SIGHT OF OTHER, LARGER THINGS. OF COURSE, SUNNY WOULD SAY THAT YOUR LIFE IS MADE UP OF YOUR DAILY EXISTENCE, AND SHE'D BE RIGHT... BUT SADLY, I DON'T THINK THAT YOUR LOVE NECESSARILY IS.

'96 Ed Brubaker

Secret Hours

When Tommy arrived in Maynardville again it had been nearly fifteen years since he'd last walked its streets.

It was a condition of his parole from debtor's prison that he return to the town of his birth—a pointless bureaucratic decision, but he'd learned long ago to stop questioning such things.

He was set-up with room and board, as well as a job as a custodian...

The town seemed smaller and emptier than he had remembered, but he knew that the population had been greatly reduced over the previous five years.

Most of the places that had ever meant anything to him were simply gone. The neighborhood he'd grown-up in was now completely different.

Places that once broke his heart to even look at had lost all significance.

SUNNY AND I KISSED FOR THE FIRST TIME SOMEWHERE AROUND HERE... I THINK...

The few teenagers he saw terrified him. They seemed to embody an ever-increasing impatience and displacement that he could only blame on computers.

But, then again, he blamed almost everything on computers.

HE STOPPED GOING OUT MUCH AFTER A WHILE.

THE GUY IN #10 KICKED THE BUCKET ... I NEED YOU TO CLEAN OUT HIS ROOM...

OKAY, I'LL GET RIGHT ON IT...

AS CHANCE WOULD HAVE IT HE MADE A GREAT DISCOVERY IN THAT ROOM...

BOOKS WERE VIRTUALLY UNHEARD OF, MOSTLY OWNED BY RICH COLLECTORS OR THE GOVERNMENT.

HOW HAD THIS BOARDER COME INTO SUCH A LIBRARY? ... THIS PRESENTED A PROBLEM: IF HE TURNED THESE OVER TO THE LANDLORD THEY WOULD BE SOLD, BUT IF HE WERE CAUGHT WITH THEM IT WOULD BE A VIOLATION OF HIS PAROLE...

AT THE END OF THE HALL LIVED TWO MEN WHO WERE BOTH NAMED STEVE. THEY WERE A BIT ECCENTRIC, BUT TOMMY FELT HE COULD TRUST THEM.

—SEE, 'CUZ TECHNICALLY THEY CAN SEARCH MY ROOM AT ANY TIME... AND I JUST—

NO, NO... IT'S NO TROUBLE.

YES, PLEASE BRING THEM IN...

EVERY NIGHT AFTER WORK HE'D GO TO THE STEVES' ROOM AND GET ANOTHER BOOK TO HIDE AWAY WITH.

HE KNEW THAT MOST OF THESE BOOKS WERE AVAILABLE TO HIM ON THE COMPUTER LIBRARY SYSTEM ...

...BUT THE STORIES, THE KNOWLEDGE, THE WISDOM, THE BEAUTY, ALL FELT SO MUCH MORE REAL AWAY FROM THE BLUE SCREEN AND ITS ELECTRIC HUM.

ONE DAY HE DISCOVERED A SMALL PILE OF COMICS AMONG THE BOOKS.

WOW, IT'S BEEN A LONG TIME SINCE I'VE SEEN ONE OF THESE...

AS A CHILD HE HAD READ ALMOST NOTHING BUT COMICS, AND STAYING UP LATE WITH THEM NOW TRANSPORTED HIM BACK TO THAT MORE INNOCENT TIME.

THERE WAS ONE COMIC IN PARTICULAR THAT HE KEPT BEING DRAWN TO. THERE WERE ONLY A FEW ISSUES OF IT, AND IT WASN'T ANY BETTER THAN MOST OF THE OTHERS, BUT THERE WAS SOMETHING FAMILIAR ABOUT IT...

...THE CHARACTERS IN IT REMINDED HIM OF HIS OLD FRIENDS AND LOVERS, ALL SO FAR AWAY... LOST IN TIME.

HE THOUGHT OF HIS DAYS WITH THEM ALL, DAYS WHEN THEY HADN'T REALIZED HOW HAPPY THEY REALLY WERE...

...BEFORE THEY HAD FALLEN THROUGH THE CRACKS IN THE NEW WORLD, BEFORE THEIR USELESSNESS HAD BECOME A LIABILITY.

HE READ THESE COMICS AGAIN AND AGAIN, AND AS HE DID HE WAS FILLED WITH LOVE AND SADNESS FOR HIS LOST FRIENDS, AND HIS LOST LIFE, AND FOR A LOST TIME.

AND THE HEARTBREAK HE COULDN'T FEEL WHEN HE LOOKED AT THE WORLD AROUND HIM WAS FOUND WITHIN THOSE PAGES, AND FOR SOME REASON THAT MADE HIM VERY HAPPY.

Ed Brubaker '96